Contents

CONTENTS

Introduction

How and when to assess

This Assessment Book provides teacher's notes and a photocopiable pupil assessment sheet for each unit (or group of units) of the programme. This structure gives the teacher complete flexibility over how and when to assess.

You may decide to use the tests as a check-up for the whole class at the end of each unit.

You may decide, every few weeks, to photocopy the relevant sheets to make a 'mini-test' that can be administered either to the whole class, groups or targeted individuals.

The questions on the test are usually styled in a different way to the other practice materials in Abacus (i.e. Textbooks and Photocopy Masters). Your daily interaction with a pupil along with their work from the practice materials will always provide the first evidence of whether he or she has particular difficulties or strengths. The assessment sheets are designed to probe a pupil's deeper understanding, presenting them with unfamiliar contexts and styles of question. The aim of the Abacus approach is to produce pupils who are confident mathematicians, and who can tackle a variety of contexts and styles, by building on what is familiar to them.

Within each teacher's section, the notes are organised under the following headings:

➤ **Skills assessed**, giving details of the exact mental and written skills covered in the unit. Key skills are the focus of the test.

➤ **Diagnostic materials**, detailing particular sections of the Textbook that directly practise the key skills identified above. These pages can be used in two ways:
- as a check of whether a particular pupil is ready for the test
- as further evidence of achievement.

➤ **Oral questions**, several questions that should be read out by the teacher at the start of the test. Answer boxes are provided on the assessment sheets. When administering the test, read each question twice, allowing about ten seconds between each reading. If you are using several different sheets as one test, you can either select a particular question from each sheet, or read out all the oral questions, with pupils recording their answers on a separate piece of paper.

➤ **Common difficulties**, giving advice on the kinds of common mistakes that pupils make, and how to remedy these.

➤ **Practice activities**, further practical activities focusing on the key skills, for pupils who need some extra reinforcement.

➤ **Follow-up materials**, where to go next for pupils who have particular difficulties or strengths.

➤ **Answers** to each test are also provided.

Each assessment sheet has a margin on the right, where you can record a pupil's score on each question. This can then be transferred to the foot of the page, and carried over, if appropriate, to the next sheet. Where pupils have answered incorrectly, but shown some understanding or relevant working, you may decide to award half a mark.

Administering the tests

An introductory page of instructions for the pupils is provided on page 5, so that you can photocopy this each time a test is administered.

No calculators are required for any of the assessment sheets, and any other special equipment needed is specified in the teacher's notes. The style of administration, e.g. formal, timed, or informal, untimed is entirely up to the individual teacher, and may be decided on a unit by unit basis. Each pupil assessment sheet will take between five and ten minutes.

Before starting, remind the pupils to read each question carefully. The assessment sheets are deliberately uncluttered and pupils can make use of any available space to work out the answer.

Tell the pupils that if they have difficulty with a question they should move on to the next one – they can always return later. If they finish the test they should always go back and check their work (if you are timing the pupils, you may wish to build in some time for this).

National Curriculum Levels

The assessment sheets can be used in a variety of ways (either one sheet at a time, or grouped together), and for this reason it is difficult to allocate particular levels to pupils' test scores.

Clearly, it is impossible to assign a level from one test sheet in isolation, and no doubt different pupils will achieve at a higher or lower level on different topics during the year. If, every few weeks, a selection of sheets is administered as one test, then over the course of the year it will become clear whether particular pupils are consistently achieving at a high or low level.

On the whole, the assessment sheets test what it would be reasonable to assume the majority can achieve during Year 4 (P5) (i.e. consolidating level 3, starting level 4 or mainly level C in Scotland).

Sensible decisions can therefore be made about pupils who regularly achieve very highly on the assessment sheets (e.g. consistently achieving 80–100% across a range of topics), those who fall into the 'middle' category (e.g. consistently in the band 60–80%) and those who have difficulties with a range of topics (e.g. consistently achieving less than 60%). You will need to make these judgements in conjunction with your everyday working knowledge of the particular pupil, and their strengths and weaknesses. You are in a unique position to decide if a test result is a 'one-off', or evidence of consistent achievement.

Instructions

- You do not need a calculator for any of the questions on these sheets.

- Work carefully through the questions.

- If you cannot do one of the questions, go on to the next one. You can come back to it later.

- When you have finished, go back and check your work.

- Read each question carefully before trying to answer.

- Use any space on the sheet to work out the answer.

Numbers to 10 000

Skills summary

- To read and write numbers to at least 10 000
- To recognise the value of each digit in numbers to 10 000
- To partition a 4-digit number into thousands, hundreds, tens and units
- To compare and order 4-digit numbers
- To use the notation < and > when comparing 4-digit numbers

Diagnostic materials

Number Textbook 1, page 3
- Check the pupils can partition and recombine 4-digit numbers including numbers where zero is a place holder.

Number Textbook 1, page 5
- Check the pupils can use and interpret < and > signs correctly.

Oral questions

1. Write the number 2307.
2. Write the number these cards make (hold up place-value cards 3000, 400, 10, 7).
3. (Write the number 2527 on the board.) Write what the 5 is worth in this number.
4. Listen to these numbers and write down the largest one: 2457, 2575.

Common difficulties

When writing numbers pupils will sometimes write the number as it is said e.g. five thousand and seventeen as '5000 17'. Use resources such as place-value cards and charts to help develop mental imagery of combining and partitioning numbers.

Pupils often confuse the greater than (>) and less than (<) signs. Encourage them to read number sentences as a class, e.g. 3600 > 2500 as *Three thousand six hundred is greater than two thousand five hundred* and point to the numbers and signs that are being read. Remind pupils of the crocodile image. *The crocodile or sign always opens its mouth to eat the larger number.*

Practice activities

1 Use number cards (0 to 9). Take four cards and write down the number formed. Rearrange the digits to make a different 4-digit number and write it down next to the first number. Put the correct sign < or > between the two numbers.

2 Roll a ten-sided dice four times to make a 4-digit number. Write down the number and partition it, e.g. 6473 = 6000 + 400 + 70 + 3.

Answers

1. 2307   **2.** 3417   **3.** 500   **4.** 2575

5. 3000, 500, 70, 1 should be circled

6. 2000, 800, 30, 3 should be circled

7. 6000, 80, 4 should be circled

8. 5000, 400, 7 should be circled

9. b, d, e should be ticked

Name _____

1. [ ]   2. [ ]   3. [ ]   4. [ ]

☐ / 4

Circle all the place-value cards that would be needed to build the number shown.

5. 3571

100   70   5   7   300   1   3000   500   50

6. 2833

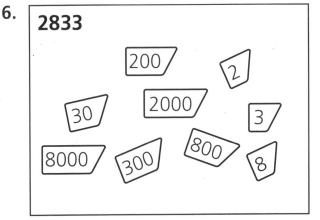

200   2   30   2000   3   8000   300   800   8

7. 6084

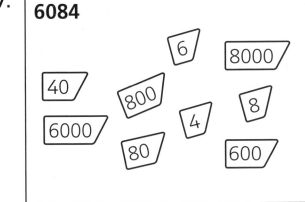

6   8000   40   800   8   6000   4   80   600

8. 5407

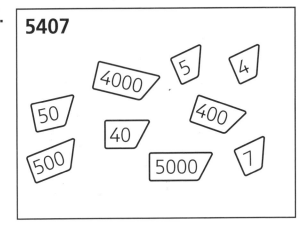

4000   5   4   50   400   40   500   5000   7

☐ / 4

---

9. Tick the number sentences that are correct.

a   434 < 243   [ ]   b   1271 > 1217   [ ]

c   4307 > 7304   [ ]   d   5124 < 6412   [ ]

e   3572 > 3527   [ ]   f   7832 < 7823   [ ]

☐ / 6

Score: [ ] / 14   Total: [ ]

Addition

Skills summary

- To know all pairs of numbers that make 10
- To know all pairs of numbers that make 20
- To know what must be added to make the next multiple of 10
- To recognise or derive quickly addition pairs to 100 (multiples of 5) or 1000 (multiples of 50)
- To recognise or derive quickly addition pairs to 100 (any 2-digit number)

Diagnostic materials

Number Textbook 1, page 8
- Check the pupils can recognise what the next 10 is and how much must be added to a number to make the next 10.

Number Textbook 1, page 15
- Check the pupils can recognise pairs of numbers that have a total of 100.

Oral questions

1. How much must be added to 56 to make the next 10?

2. What must be added to 35 to make 100?

3. A man has to walk 1000 m to reach his destination. He has walked 450 m. How much further has he to go?

4. When added together two numbers have a total of 100. One of the numbers is 57. What is the other number?

Common difficulties

Pupils need plenty of practice to learn number bonds to 10 and 20. They also need to be given opportunities to make connections between number facts. Chanting complements to 10, the next 10 and 100 can help, e.g. say a number, ask the children to chant how many to make 10 or the next 10, *Seven, three; Seventeen, three; Twenty-seven, three*, etc.

Use a 100 square to build up complements to 100. *How many to the next ten? How many to one hundred?*

Practice activities

1 Use number cards (10 to 99). Take a card, write down the number and how much must be added to make the next ten, e.g. 26 + 4 = 30.

2 Use number cards. Take a selection of number cards (about 20) that have pairs of numbers that make 100. Match pairs of numbers that total 100.

Answers

1. 4	**2.** 65	**3.** 550 m	**4.** 43
5. 20	**6.** 8	**7.** 15	**8.** 16

9. join 450 and 550, 200 and 800, 700 and 300, 650 and 350

10. circle a, b, f

Name _____

1. [   ]   2. [   ]   3. [   ]   4. [   ]

⬚/4

Complete the additions below.

5. 7 + 13 = ____   6. 12 + ____ = 20

7. 20 = 5 + ____   8. 4 + ____ = 20

⬚/4

9. Join pairs that make 1000 (some numbers may not join
    to other numbers).

450   300
200   950
150   800
700   350
650   550

⬚/4

10. Circle the pairs that total 100.

a 35, 65   b 20, 80   c 45, 65

d 28, 82   e 63, 47   f 19, 81

⬚/6

Score: [   ] /18   Total: [   ]

Addition and subtraction

Skills summary
- To find a small difference by counting up from the smaller number to the larger one
- To add several 1-digit numbers by finding pairs that total 9, 10 or 11

Diagnostic materials
Number Textbook 1, page 11
- Check the pupils can find a small difference by counting without the aid of a number line.

Number Textbook 1, page 18
- Check the pupils can and do add several 1-digit numbers by finding pairs that total 9, 10 or 11.

Oral questions
1. Find the difference between 132 and 127.
2. How much more than 146 is 153?
3. Listen to these numbers. Which two have a total of 11: 3, 7, 8, 9?
4. Find the total of 4, 5 and 7.

Common difficulties
Pupils often find the word 'difference' difficult to understand. It is more effective to demonstrate what difference means, e.g. by using two towers of interlocking cubes and making a comparison, rather than simply saying difference means subtract.

Some pupils will continue to rely on strategies such as counting on or using fingers to add several 1-digit numbers as it is a strategy they are comfortable with. To move some pupils on, show them how it is quicker to find pairs that make 9, 10 or 11 rather than counting on in ones.

Practice activities
1 Use number cards (10 to 99). Take two cards and find the difference between them by counting up in ones and tens as necessary.

2 Roll a ten-sided dice four or five times. Write down the numbers rolled as a number sentence and find the total by finding pairs that make 9, 10 or 11, e.g. 5 + 3 + 6 + 7 + 2 = 11 + 3 + 9 = 20 + 3 = 23.

Answers

1. 5	**2.** 7	**3.** 3, 8	**4.** 16
5. 3	**6.** 6	**7.** 18	**8.** 15
9. join a to g, b to e, c to h, d to f			
10. 21	**11.** 24	**12.** 22	**13.** 21
14. 23	**15.** 16		

Name _____

1. [ ]   2. [ ]   3. [ ]   4. [ ]

[ ]/4

Write in the box the difference between the numbers on each number line.

5.
128   131 [ ]

6.
247   253 [ ]

7.
465   483 [ ]

8.
397   412 [ ]

[ ]/4

9. Join the calculations that have the same difference.

a 102 − 95   e 134 − 124

b 213 − 203   f 151 − 146

c 253 − 245   g 312 − 305

d 313 − 308   h 267 − 259

[ ]/4

Calculate the total for each addition.

10. 3 + 7 + 5 + 6 = _____   11. 2 + 9 + 6 + 7 = _____

12. 4 + 5 + 6 + 7 = _____   13. 7 + 8 + 2 + 4 = _____

14. 9 + 6 + 4 + 4 = _____   15. 6 + 2 + 3 + 5 = _____

[ ]/6

Score: [ ] /18   Total: [ ]

Number sequences

Skills summary

- To count on or back in ones to 1000
- To recognise and extend number sequences counting on or back in 50s from any number to 1000
- To recognise and extend number sequences counting on or back in 25s from any number to 1000

Diagnostic materials

Number Textbook 1, page 20, questions 1 to 12
- Check the pupils can understand '1 more than' and '1 less than', and know the number before and after a given 3-digit number.

Number Textbook 1, page 21, questions 14 to 19
- Check the pupils can calculate 50 more or less than a given 3-digit number.

Oral questions

1. Write the next number in the sequence: 275, 300, 325.
2. What is 50 more than 385?
3. Which number comes before 480?
4. (Write on the board 286, 261, 236, 211, 186.) Which number comes next in the sequence?

Common difficulties

Pupils find it more difficult to work out the next number in the sequence if they are unaware of the pattern in the sequence. For example, when counting in 50s the tens digit and the units digit are the same on every other number in the sequence, e.g. 37, 87, 137, 187, etc. When counting in 25s, the last two digits are the same in every fourth number, e.g. 50, 75, 100, 125, 150, 175, 200.

Pupils also need to experience a wide range of vocabulary: before, after, sequence, next, consecutive, etc.

Practice activities

1 Use number cards (10 to 99). Take a card and roll a six-sided dice. Write down the number on the card and count up in 50s or 25s the number of times shown on the dice, e.g. 43 picked and 4 rolled makes the count: 43, 93, 143, 193, 243.

2 Use number cards (0 to 9). Take three cards to form a 3-digit number. Write down the number and the number that comes before it and the number that comes after it.

Answers			
1. 350	**2.** 435	**3.** 479	**4.** 161
5. 398, 400, 401	**6.** 529, 528, 527	**7.** 270, 370	**8.** 345, 495
9. 205, 230	**10.** 265, 215	**11.** 5, 105	**12.** 84, 184
13. 217, 317	**14.** 262, 362	**15.** 10, 60	**16.** 135, 185
17. 102, 152	**18.** 218, 268		

Name _____

1. [____]   2. [____]   3. [____]   4. [____]

$\frac{\boxed{}}{4}$

Complete the sequences below.

5. 396, 397, _____, 399, _____, _____

6. 532, 531, 530, _____, _____, _____

7. 120, 170, 220, _____, 320, _____

8. 245, 295, _____, 395, 445, _____

9. 80, 105, 130, 155, 180, _____, _____

10. 340, 315, 290, _____, 240, _____

$\frac{\boxed{}}{14}$

Write the number 50 less and the number 50 more than the number shown.

11. _____ 55 _____   12. _____ 134 _____

13. _____ 267 _____   14. _____ 312 _____

$\frac{\boxed{}}{8}$

Write the number 25 less and the number 25 more than the number shown.

15. _____ 35 _____   16. _____ 160 _____

17. _____ 127 _____   18. _____ 243 _____

$\frac{\boxed{}}{8}$

Abacus Ginn and Company 2000.
Copying permitted for purchasing school only.
This material is not copyright free.

Score: [____] /34   Total: [____]

Multiplication and division

Skills summary

- To recognise the relationship between multiplication and division
- To recognise the relationship between multiplication and addition
- To recognise the relationship between division and subtraction
- To recognise and use the commutativity of multiplication
- To recognise the concept of multiplication through arrays

Diagnostic materials

Number Textbook 1, page 23
- Check the pupils recognise the concept of multiplication through arrays and can recognise arrays that are equivalent.

Number Textbook 1, page 27, questions 1 to 10
- Check the pupils recognise division as grouping.

Oral questions

1. What are 4 lots of 5?
2. In a shop beans are stacked in 3 rows. There are 6 tins in a row. How many tins are on the shelf?
3. 30 children sit in rows of 5. How many rows are there?
4. How many lots of 4 in 24?

Common difficulties

Children will find multiplication and division as repeated addition and subtraction more difficult if they are not confident with counting on and back in multiples of different numbers. Use fingers to keep track of the count.

It is important to show children that they will get the same answer by using repeated addition as by using multiplication. Using the constant function on a calculator for repeated addition can help show children how important it is to learn multiplication facts and that repeated addition in a much longer process.

Practice activities

1 Use number cards (2, 3, 4, 5, 10). Take a card and roll a ten-sided dice. Write the multiplication, e.g. $2 \times 6 = 12$ and write the equivalent multiplication and the corresponding divisions.

2 Generate multiplications as above and draw a corresponding array, e.g. 3×4 shaded in squares as 3 rows of 4.

Answers

1. 20   2. 18   3. 6   4. 6
5. join a to g, b to e, c to h, d to f
6. 12   20   3   7. 30   2   6

Name _____

I.   **2.**   **3.**   **4.**

4

5. Join each calculation to its array.

   a   3 × 7   **b**   4 × 5   **c**   6 × 4   **d**   7 × 2

e 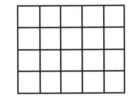   **f** 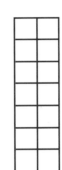   **g** 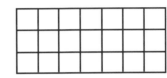   **h**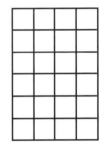

4

Complete the diagrams below. The numbers in the circles are multiplied to give a number in the square.

6. 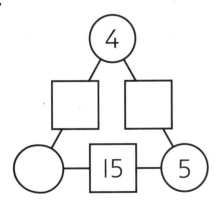   **7.**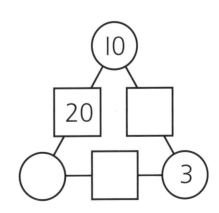

6

Score: [ ] /14   Total: [ ]

Multiplication and division

Skills summary

- To use knowledge of multiplication and division facts for ×2, ×3, ×4, ×5 and ×10 tables
- To derive ×8 table by doubling ×4 table
- To derive division facts corresponding to ×8 table
- To double or halve a 2-digit number by doubling/halving the tens first

Diagnostic materials

Number Textbook 1, page 33, questions 1 to 10
- Check pupils can use knowledge of multiplication and division facts to complete missing number problems.

Number Textbook 1, page 34
- Check pupils can double and halve given 2-digit numbers by doubling or halving the most significant digit first.

Oral questions

1. If I know 4 lots of 7 are 28, what are 8 lots of 7?
2. How many 8s in 32?
3. Double 26.
4. Find half of 68.

Common difficulties

Children struggle to learn all their tables if they have to learn each one as an individual fact. Encourage them to make connections between the tables so that there are fewer facts to learn, e.g. to calculate ×4, double and double again.

Often children find it more difficult to double a number where they have to bridge a ten. Partitioning the numbers into tens and units enables children to see more easily the value of the digits so that they can double the values before recombining.

Practice activities

1 Roll a ten-sided dice, multiply the number by 4 and then 8. Write down number sentences, e.g. 4 × 6 = 24, 8 × 6 = 48.

2 Use number cards (10 to 99). Take two cards. If an odd number is picked double it. If an even number is picked halve it. Record the numbers and their half or double. How long does it take to do 20?

Answers

1. 56   **2.** 4   **3.** 52   **4.** 34
5. top row   20, 12   middle row   20, 30   bottom row   6, 15
6. 12   24   **7.** 24   48   **8.** 28   56   **9.** 36   72
10. reading from the left   24   54   23   26   76   46

Name _____

I. [   ]   **2.** [   ]   **3.** [   ]   **4.** [   ]

4

5. Complete this multiplication grid.

×	2	5	3
4	8		
10		50	
3			q

6

Complete these calculations.

6.   4 × 3 = _____   8 × 3 = _____

7.   4 × 6 = _____   8 × 6 = _____

8.   4 × 7 = _____   8 × 7 = _____

q.   4 × q = _____   8 × q = _____

8

I0. A function machine doubles the numbers that are put into it.
Complete the table so that 'output' is always double 'input'.

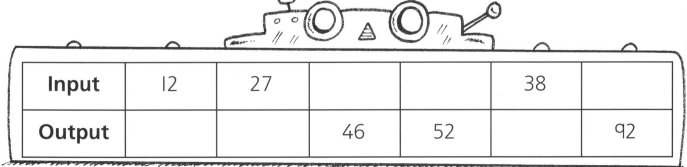

Input	I2	27			38	
Output			46	52		q2

6

Score: [   ] /24   Total: [   ]

Fractions

Skills summary

- To use fraction notation for non-unitary fractions
- To use fraction notation for mixed numbers
- To recognise when two simple fractions are equivalent

Diagnostic materials

Number Textbook 1, page 43
- Check pupils are able to recognise the proportion of objects as a fraction in relation to the whole.

Number Textbook 1, page 46, questions 1 to 9
- Check pupils are able to use knowledge of equivalence to fill in missing numerators or denominators to make fractions equal.

Oral questions

1. I am thinking of a shape. Three quarters of it is shaded. How much of the shape is not shaded?
2. In a group of 6 children 3 of the children are girls. What fraction of the group is girls?
3. How many quarters are there in $1\frac{1}{4}$?
4. Which of these fractions is equivalent to one third – $\frac{2}{4}$, $\frac{3}{9}$, $\frac{4}{9}$ or $\frac{9}{12}$?

Common difficulties

Use a range of images to develop an understanding of fractions. Pupils need to realise that with fractions they are looking at a given number of equal parts. Use a variety of folded and shaded shapes, emphasising that the shape is divided into a number of equal parts (the denominator) and that they are looking at a number of those parts (the numerator).

Use similar shapes to help develop an understanding of equivalence. Fold shapes into halves, quarters and eighths and make direct comparisons.

Practice activities

1. Roll a ten-sided dice and a six-sided dice. Write the smaller number above the larger one to form a fraction. Draw a shape and shade in the fraction created by the dice rolls.

2. Generate a fraction by rolling two six-sided dice. Write the smaller number above the larger one and then write an equivalent fraction next to it, e.g. $\frac{2}{5} = \frac{4}{10}$.

Answers

1. $\frac{1}{4}$ 2. $\frac{1}{2}$ or $\frac{3}{6}$ 3. 5 quarters   4. $\frac{3}{9}$

5–10. check the correct amount is shaded

11, 15 and 16 should be ticked

Name _____

1.   2.   3.   4.

$$\frac{\square}{4}$$

Shade the fraction shown for each shape.

5.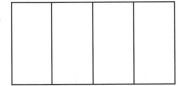

$$\frac{3}{4}$$

6.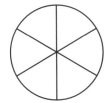

$$\frac{5}{6}$$

7.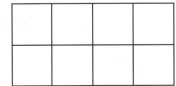

$$\frac{3}{8}$$

8.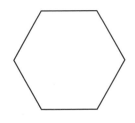

$$\frac{1}{6}$$

9.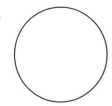

$$\frac{5}{8}$$

10.

$$\frac{4}{9}$$

$$\frac{\square}{6}$$

Tick the fractions that are equivalent.

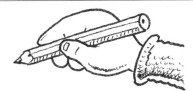

11. $\frac{1}{3} = \frac{3}{9}$ 12. $\frac{3}{4} = \frac{8}{12}$ 13. $\frac{2}{5} = \frac{2}{10}$

14. $\frac{2}{7} = \frac{4}{7}$ ☐   15. $\frac{3}{5} = \frac{6}{10}$ 16. $\frac{5}{6} = \frac{10}{12}$

$$\frac{\square}{6}$$

Score: ☐ /16   Total: ☐

Addition and subtraction

Skills summary

- To add or subtract multiples of 10
- To add or subtract multiples of 100
- To add near multiples of 10 to 2- or 3-digit numbers
- To subtract near multiples of 10 from 2- or 3-digit numbers

Diagnostic materials

Number Textbook 1, page 47, questions 1 to 10
- Check pupils can add near multiples of 10 to a 2-digit number using the 100 square as support if necessary.

Number Textbook 1, page 52, questions 1 to 10; page 54, questions 1 to 10
- Check pupils can add or subtract multiples of 10 and 100 by using knowledge of addition and subtraction of small numbers.

Oral questions

1. Find the total of 36 and 29.
2. What is 19 less than 53?
3. A car costs £1200. John has £700. How much more does he need to buy the car?
4. What is 150 more than 170?

Common difficulties

Children will find adding and subtracting near multiples of 10 easier if they understand why the adjustment works and not just how to do it. For example, 56 + 29 = 56 + 30 – 1 because 29 = 30 – 1.

Making connections between different calculations ensures that children have to learn fewer facts e.g. 3 + 7 = 10, so 30 + 70 = 100, etc. Make connections explicit by asking children questions in sequences and then discussing what they notice or by writing questions in a sequence on the board e.g. 12 + 7 = 19, 120 + 70 = 190, etc.

Practice activities

1 Use number cards. Give children two sets of number cards, one with near multiples of 10 and one with other 2-digit numbers. Take a card from each pile and find the total or the difference (if finding the difference, ensure the numbers of the other 2-digit cards are larger than those of the near multiples).

2 Use number cards (1 to 20). Take two cards and write down the addition e.g. 14 + 9 = 23. Then write down additions for multiples of 10, i.e. 140 + 90 etc. Continue for multiples of 100, then repeat choosing two new cards.

Answers			
1. 65	**2.** 34	**3.** £500	**4.** 320
5. 80	**6.** 900	**7.** 80	**8.** 230
9. 500	**10.** 2200		
11. join a to f, b to h, c to e, d to g			
12. b should be ticked			

Name _____

1. [ ]   2. [ ]   3. [ ]   4. [ ]

$$\frac{\square}{4}$$

Complete the calculations below.

5. 130 + _____ = 210   6. _____ + 600 = 1500

7. 240 − _____ = 160   8. _____ − 60 = 170

9. 1800 + _____ = 2300   10. _____ − 500 = 1700

$$\frac{\square}{6}$$

11. Join calculations that give the same answer.

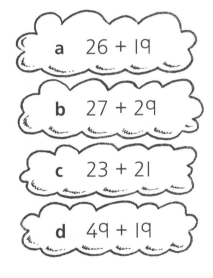

a   26 + 19   e   65 − 21

b   27 + 29   f   64 − 19

c   23 + 21   g   97 − 29

d   49 + 19   h   84 − 28

$$\frac{\square}{4}$$

12. Tick the questions that give an answer of 154.

a   125 + 30 [ ]   b   105 + 49 [ ]

c   163 − 19 [ ]   d   183 − 39 [ ]

$$\frac{\square}{4}$$

Score: [ ] /18   Total: [ ]

Numbers to 10 000

Skills summary

- To count on or back in 10s, 100s or 1000s from any number up to 10 000
- To recognise 1 more or less than any number up to 10 000
- To recognise 10 more or less than any number up to 10 000
- To recognise 100 more or less than any number up to 10 000
- To recognise 1000 more or less than any number up to 10 000

Diagnostic materials

Number Textbook 1, page 57, questions 1 to 12
- Check pupils can recognise patterns in numbers and complete them by adding/subtracting 1, 10, 100 or 1000.

Oral questions

1. Write the next number in this sequence 78, 88, 98, ...

2. I am thinking of a number. I add 100 to it and the answer I get is 437. What number am I thinking of?

3. 1000 less than a number is 2005. What is that number?

4. What is 10 less than 403?

Common difficulties

Pupils who do not understand place-value find if difficult to add or subtract 1, 10, 100 or 1000 to or from a given number. Use place-value cards and ensure that children are encouraged to read the whole number rather than a set of digits, e.g. 'three hundred and sixty-seven' rather than 'three six seven'. Look at patterns in numbers, e.g. using the constant function on a calculator. Ask children questions like *What happens when we go up in hundreds from a number?* and *What do you notice about the number in the hundreds column?*

Practice activities

1 Use number cards (0 to 9). Take three or four number cards to form a 3- or 4-digit number. Write down the number and 1 more, 1 less, 10 more, 10 less, 100 more, 100 less.

2 Use cards (+10, –10, +100, –100, +1000, –1000). Roll a dice three times to generate a 3-digit number and take a card. Write down the number generated by the dice and the next three in the sequence, jumping in steps according to the card chosen, e.g. 368 + 10 → 378, 388, 398.

Answers			
1. 108	**2.** 337	**3.** 3005	**4.** 393
5. Reading from the left 85 158 226 492 807			
6. Reading from the left 239 1330 1250 3080 2998			
7. 364, 368	**8.** 746, 726	**9.** 800, 799	
10. 2097, 2117	**11.** 3724, 3824	**12.** 5965, 5765	

Name _____

1. [ ]   2. [ ]   3. [ ]   4. [ ]

Complete the tables for the function machines below.

5.   The first adds 10 to the number put in.

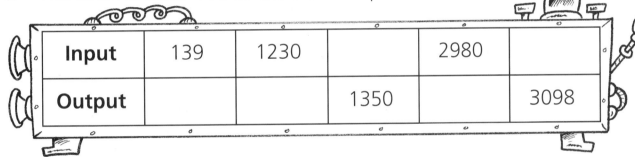

Input	75	148			797
Output			236	502	

6.   The second adds 100 to the number put in.

Input	139	1230		2980	
Output			1350		3098

Complete each of the sequences below.

7.   _____ 365, 366, 367, _____, 369

8.   786, 776, 766, 756, _____, 736, _____

9.   803, 802, 801, _____, _____, 798

10.   2067, 2077, 2087, _____, 2107, _____

11.   3424, 3524, 3624, _____, _____, 3924

12.   6265, 6165, 6065, _____, 5865, _____

Score: [ ] /26   Total: [ ]

Addition.

Skills summary

- To partition 2-digit numbers into tens and units to add
- To add several 2-digit numbers by adding the most significant digit first
- To add multiples of 10 to 2- or 3-digit numbers
- To add 2- or 3-digit numbers to multiples of 10, 100 or 1000

Diagnostic materials

Number Textbook 1, page 59, questions 1 to 7
- Check pupils can add several numbers to find given totals.

Number Textbook 1, page 63, questions 1 to 9
- Check pupils can use knowledge of place-value to add a multiple of 10 to a 3-digit number.

Oral questions

1. Find the total of 26, 24 and 17.
2. Simon buys a bag of crisps for 25p, a chocolate bar for 35p and a drink for 28p. How much does he spend?
3. Add 60 to 245.
4. Tom has saved £167. He receives £50 for his birthday and adds it to his savings. How much does he have altogether?

Common difficulties

Children may have difficulty holding several numbers in their head to add them up. Suggest that they add the tens first and then the units (or vice versa) and then combine the two totals. Show them how to jot down each step, e.g. 25 + 37 + 32 = 80 + 14 = 94 ensuring that the equals signs are in the correct place. This will help children to organise their thoughts. Some pupils will only need to do this a few times before the process is clear and they can complete all the steps without any jottings.

Pupils who are less secure with place-value can become confused when adding two numbers with a different number of digits. Ensure that they read the whole numbers and emphasise the value of the digits.

Practice activities

1 Use number cards (10 to 99). Take three cards and find their total. Repeat several times.

2 Use number cards (10, 20, 30, ... 90). Roll three dice to form a 3-digit number and take a card. Write down the two numbers and find their total.

Answers			
1. 67	**2.** 88p	**3.** 305	**4.** £217
5. 99p	**6.** 112p or £1·12	**7.** 84p	**8.** 93p
9. top row 183, 257 middle row 146, 277 bottom row 176, 233			

Name _____

I. [ ]   **2.** [ ]   **3.** [ ]   **4.** [ ]

☐
—
4

pack of stickers	can of drink	comic	pencil	pack of gum	bar of chocolate
25p	36p	49p	19p	27p	38p

Find the total cost of the three items listed:

5. can of drink, bar of chocolate, pack of stickers _____

6. comic, can of drink, pack of gum _____

7. pack of gum, bar of chocolate, pencil _____

8. comic, pencil, pack of stickers _____

☐
—
4

9. Complete the table below.

+	86	143	217
40	126		
60		203	
90			307

☐
—
6

Score: [ ] /14   Total: [ ]

Subtraction

Skills summary

- To find the difference between two 2-digit numbers by counting up through multiples of 10
- To subtract a 2-digit number from another 2-digit number

Diagnostic materials

Number Textbook 1, page 65
- Check pupils can find the difference between two 2-digit numbers, using the number line as support if necessary.

Number Textbook 1, page 68
- Check pupils use an appropriate strategy – counting on, counting back, rounding – to subtract a number from a 2-digit number.

Oral questions

1. Find the difference between 37 and 51.
2. How much more than 26 is 43?
3. Subtract 29 from 54.
4. What is 39 less than 82?

Common difficulties

There are many skills involved in counting up through the next multiple – knowing the next multiple of 10, knowing how many to the next multiple and being able to count up in tens. Use a 100 square to look at what the next ten is and how many to the next ten. It is also important to make connections – ask children to chant back the answer as a class. *How many to the next ten from 27? Three. What about 37 or 47?*, etc.

Provide opportunities for pupils to discuss the different methods they have used. Demonstrate how using a rounding strategy may be quicker than counting up or back when working with particular numbers.

Practice activities

1 Use number cards. Give children five number cards with numbers over 50 whose units are between 1 and 4, and another five with numbers less than 50 whose units are between 6 and 9. The children take a card from each set and find the difference between the two numbers.

2 Use number cards (10 to 99). Give children 20 number cards. The children take two cards and write the subtraction taking the smaller number from the larger one, e.g. 72 – 21. They calculate the answer using jottings.

Answers

1. 14	**2.** 17	**3.** 25	**4.** 43
5. 16	**6.** 27	**7.** 34	**8.** 47
9. 15	**10.** 26	**11.** 35	**12.** 39
13. 14	**14.** 22		

Name _____

1. [ ]   2. [ ]   3. [ ]   4. [ ]

4

Calculate the difference between the numbers shown.

5. 38   54 · difference = _____

6. 46   73   difference = _____

7. 31   65   difference = _____

8. 45   92   difference = _____

4

Complete these calculations.

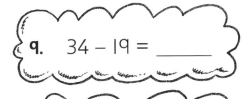
9.   34 – 19 = _____

10.   42 – 16 = _____

11.   63 – 28 = _____

12.   87 – 48 = _____

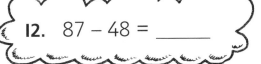
13.   81 – 67 = _____

14.   91 – 69 = _____

6

Score: [ ] /14   Total: [ ]

Multiples

Skills summary

- To count on or back in 2s, 3s, 4s, 5s, 10s
- To recognise multiples of 2, 3, 4, 5 and 10 up to the tenth multiple

Diagnostic materials

Number Textbook 2, page 3, questions 1 to 9
- Check pupils are able to count in 2s on or back from a given even number.

Number Textbook 2, page 4, questions 1 to 17
- Check pupils are able to recognise the next multiple of 5 after a given number.

Oral questions

1. Write the next number in this sequence: 18, 21, 24, ...
2. Listen to these numbers: 31, 36, 45. Which one is a multiple of 5?
3. What is the next multiple of 10 after 37?
4. Write down the third multiple of 4.

Common difficulties

Pupils need to have opportunities to count forwards and backwards in steps of different sizes from different starting numbers, i.e. not always starting the count forwards from zero.

Pupils usually find it easier to recognise multiples of 2 (because they are even numbers), 5 (because they end in 5 or 0) and 10 (because they end in 0). They have more difficulty with 3 and 4, often assuming that if a number ends in 3 or 4 it is a multiple of 3 or 4. These misconceptions should be confronted e.g. by putting multiples of 3 on a washing line together with numbers that are not multiples of 3, putting them in order and talking about which numbers should be there and which should not.

Practice activities

1 Roll two ten-sided dice to make a 2-digit number. Tally the number of times a multiple of 2, 3, 4, 5 or 10 comes up. After 30 rolls, which number has had the most multiples rolled?

2 Use number cards (2-digit multiples of 2, 3, 4, and 5). Take a card and decide of which number it is a multiple. Write the next three multiples of that number, e.g. pick card 27 and write 30, 33, 36, etc.

Answers

1. 27	**2.** 45	**3.** 40	**4.** 12
5. 40, 50, 60, 65		**6.** 15, 27, 30	
7. 28, 26, 20		**8.** 32, 36, 44	

9. check circles/squares are drawn around the correct numbers
   12 and 24 have squares and circles on them

Name _____

1. [ ]   2. [ ]   3. [ ]   4. [ ]

[ ]
4

Fill in the missing numbers in the sequences below.

5. 25, 30, 35, _____, 45, _____, 55, _____, _____

6. 12, _____, 18, 21, 24, _____, _____

7. 30, _____, _____, 24, 22, _____

8. 20, 24, 28, _____, _____, 40, _____, 48

[ ]
13

---

9. In the table below:

– draw a circle ◯ around the multiples of 3

– draw a square ☐ around the multiples of 4

18	5	15	16
7	12	19	30
24	17	40	27
11	32	6	23

Which numbers have squares and circles on them? _____

[ ]
14

Score: [ ] /31   Total: [ ]

Multiplication facts

Skills summary·

- To use knowledge of ×3, ×6, ×7 and ×9 tables
- To use division facts for ×3, ×6, ×7 and ×9 tables
- To derive ×6 table by doubling ×3 table
- To construct a multiplication square

Diagnostic materials

Number Textbook 2, page 7, questions 11 to 23
- Check pupils can use knowledge of ×6 table to complete number sentences involving multiplication and division.

Number Textbook 2, page 14, multiplication square
- Check pupils can complete the multiplication square correctly.

Oral questions

1. If 7 × 3 is 21, what is 7 × 6?
2. How many lots of 3 are there in 24?
3. What is 4 × 9?
4. Pencils come in packets of 6. How many packets would be needed for 36 pencils?

Common difficulties

Learning tables as a series of individual facts can be quite an onerous task. If children are taught the connections between the tables, they will have a greater understanding and have fewer facts to learn. For example, they can learn that the ×6 table can be derived by doubling the ×3 table. Similarly, the ×9 table can be derived by taking away one lot of the multiplier from the ×10 table, e.g. 7 × 9 = 7 × 10 – 7.

Pupils need to practise chanting the multiples of numbers and the complete tables to help memorise the facts.

Practice activities

1 Choose one of the tables ×3, ×6, ×7 or ×9. Roll a ten-sided dice and multiply the number rolled by the chosen table number, e.g. 5 × 7. Write down the answer. How many rolls does it take before you have rolled all the calculations from 1 to 9?

2 Use number cards (3, 6, 7, 9). Take a card and roll a ten-sided dice. Write down the calculation generated, e.g. 6 × 9 = 54 and the corresponding division, i.e. 54 ÷ 9 = 6.

Answers

1. 42   **2.** 8   **3.** 36   **4.** 6
5. join a to i, b to j, c to g, d to k, e to l, f to h
6. first column 18, 27   second column 18, 42, 72

Name _____

1. [ ]   2. [ ]   3. [ ]   4. [ ]

□/4

5. Join calculations that give the same **answer**.

a 24 ÷ 4

b 6 × 6

c 5 × 6

d 42 ÷ 6

e 45 ÷ 9

f 3 × 6

g 3 × 10

h 2 × 9

i 36 ÷ 6

j 4 × 9

k 21 ÷ 3

l 35 ÷ 7

□/6

6. Complete the table below.

	×3	×6
3	9	
6		36
7	21	
9		54
12	36	

□/5

Score: [ ] /15   Total: [ ]

Multiplication and division

Skills summary

- To multiply or divide any integer up to 1000 by 10 (whole number answers)
- To multiply any integer up to 1000 by 100
- To partition numbers into tens and units and then multiply

Diagnostic materials

Number Textbook 2, page 16
- Check pupils can use their knowledge of multiplying/dividing by 10 in the context of money and measures.

Number Textbook 2, page 18
- Check pupils can multiply a 2-digit multiple of 10 by a 1-digit number.

Oral questions

1. Multiply 37 by 10.

2. I am thinking of a number. I multiply it by 10 and the answer I get is 2300. What number am I thinking of?

3. What are 4 lots of 30?

4. I buy 3 stamps at 26p each. How much do I spend?

Common difficulties

Pupils who are taught to multiply by 10 or 100 by adding zeros to the number are likely to come unstuck later when they work with decimal numbers. It is important that they understand that the digits move one place to the left when a number is multiplied by 10 because the value of each digit is ten times bigger.

If children are not secure with their tables facts they will find it difficult to multiply multiples of 10. They need to continue practising their tables even when they have moved on to working with larger numbers.

Practice activities

1 Roll three ten-sided dice to form a 3-digit number. Multiply the number rolled by 10. Write down the answer. Repeat ten times. Look at the numbers written down and divide each one by 10.

2 Use number cards (20 to 40). Take a card and roll a six-sided dice (if 1 is rolled, roll again). Write down the multiplication, e.g. 23 × 4 and calculate the answer. Repeat several times.

Answers			
1. 370	**2.** 230	**3.** 120	**4.** 78p
5. 360	**6.** 53	**7.** 10	**8.** 4700
9. 100	**10.** 10	**11.** 540	**12.** 29
13. a, b, e and f should be ticked			
14. 120	**15.** 300	**16.** 120	**17.** 140

Name _____

1. [   ]   2. [   ]   3. [   ]   4. [   ]

$\boxed{}$
4

Complete these calculations.

5. $36 \times 10 =$ _____

6. _____ $\times 10 = 530$

7. $300 \div$ _____ $= 30$

8. $47 \times 100 =$ _____

9. $71 \times$ _____ $= 7100$

10. $68 \times$ _____ $= 680$

11. _____ $\div 10 = 54$

12. _____ $\times 100 = 2900$

$\boxed{}$
8

13. Tick the calculations that are correct.

a $15 \times 4 = 60$ [   ]

b $22 \times 3 = 66$ [   ]

c $27 \times 3 = 89$ [   ]

d $31 \times 3 = 94$ [   ]

e $42 \times 3 = 126$ [   ]

f $28 \times 5 = 140$ [   ]

$\boxed{}$
6

Circle the correct answer for each calculation.

14. 3×40 12   120   1200

15. 6×50 300   3000   30000

16. 4×30 120   1200   12000

17. 7×20 14   140   1400

$\boxed{}$
4

Score: [   ] /22   Total: [   ]

Fractions

Skills summary

- To recognise equivalence in simple fractions
- To compare and order fractions
- To position fractions on a number line
- To find fractions of numbers and quantities
- To begin to relate fractions to division

Diagnostic materials

Number Textbook 2, page 23, fraction lines
- Check pupils can identify fractions marked on a number line.

Number Textbook 2, page 24
- Check pupils can find fraction amounts of coins, using pictures to support as necessary.

Oral questions

1. Write the fraction equivalent to one quarter – $\frac{2}{4}$, $\frac{2}{8}$, or $\frac{2}{6}$.
2. (Draw a number line on the board, putting 0 at one end, 1 at the other, and a mark three quarters of the way along.) What fraction is marked on this line?
3. What is one third of 9?
4. John has 25p left. It is a quarter of his pocket money. How much pocket money is he given?

Common difficulties

Children often become confused when working with fractions. It is common to think that the larger the denominator or the numerator the larger the fraction must be. Use pictorial representation of fractions to help pupils to make comparisons.

Some children may not realise that fractions require amounts to be divided into groups of equal sizes. Encourage them to check this. Non-unitary fractions, e.g. $\frac{2}{3}$, often cause problems because they require a two-step operation. Use counters or cubes to show how to divide an amount into 3 groups and then combine 2 of them to give the answer.

Practice activities

1 Roll two ten-sided dice. Write the smaller digit above the larger one, then draw and shade a shape to represent the fraction. Repeat. Decide which is the larger fraction.

2 Using the numbers from 21 to 30, investigate which ones give a whole number answer when divided into halves, quarters or thirds.

Answers

1. $\frac{2}{8}$ 2. $\frac{3}{4}$ 3. 3   4. £1 or 100p

5. check fractions are in the correct position on the number line

6. $\frac{2}{6}$, $\frac{3}{9}$ 7. $\frac{2}{4}$, $\frac{4}{8}$ 8. $\frac{2}{8}$, $\frac{3}{12}$

9. $\frac{1}{4}$ 10. $\frac{1}{5}$ 11. $\frac{3}{4}$ 12. $\frac{1}{3}$

13. join a to e, b to g, c to h, d to f

Name _____

1. [ ]   **2.** [ ]   **3.** [ ]   **4.** [ ]

$\dfrac{\ }{4}$

5. Mark these fractions on the number line.

   a $\dfrac{1}{2}$ **b** $\dfrac{1}{4}$ **c** $\dfrac{3}{4}$ **d** $\dfrac{1}{3}$

0 |

$\dfrac{\ }{4}$

Circle the fractions that are equivalent to the first fraction.

6. $\dfrac{1}{3} = \dfrac{2}{6}\ \ \dfrac{1}{6}\ \ \dfrac{2}{3}\ \ \dfrac{3}{9}$ **7.** $\dfrac{1}{2} = \dfrac{1}{4}\ \ \dfrac{2}{4}\ \ \dfrac{4}{8}\ \ \dfrac{1}{3}$

            8. $\dfrac{1}{4} = \dfrac{1}{2}\ \ \dfrac{1}{6}\ \ \dfrac{2}{8}\ \ \dfrac{3}{12}$

$\dfrac{\ }{6}$

Complete the number sentences using the correct fraction from the ones listed: $\dfrac{1}{2}\ \dfrac{1}{3}\ \dfrac{1}{4}\ \dfrac{1}{5}\ \dfrac{2}{3}\ \dfrac{3}{4}$

9. __ of 12p = 3p   **10.** __ of 50p = 10p

11. __ of £1·00 = 75p   **12.** __ of 60p = 20p

$\dfrac{\ }{4}$

13. Join calculations that will give the same answer.

  a 60 ÷ 3   **b** 60 ÷ 2   **c** 60 ÷ 5   **d** 60 ÷ 4

  e $\dfrac{1}{3}$ of 60   **f** $\dfrac{1}{4}$ of 60   **g** $\dfrac{1}{2}$ of 60   **h** $\dfrac{1}{5}$ of 60

$\dfrac{\ }{4}$

Score: [ ] /22   Total: [ ]

Rounding

Skills summary

- To round a 3-digit number to the nearest ten
- To round a 3-digit number to the nearest hundred

Diagnostic materials

Number Textbook 2, page 27
- Check pupils can interpret the numbers represented on a number line.

Number Textbook 2, page 29, questions 1 to 10
- Check pupils are able to round given amounts of money to the nearest 10p and nearest £1.

Oral questions

1. How much is 75 to the nearest ten?

2. Between which two hundreds does 358 lie?

3. Write 652 to the nearest hundred.

4. How much more is it from 270 to the next hundred?

Common difficulties

Rounding 5 or 50 can cause problems. Children need to be taught explicitly that 5 rounds up to the nearest ten and 50 rounds up to the nearest hundred. When rounding to the nearest hundred, children can become confused by first trying to round the units, e.g. when rounding 347 a common misconception is to round to the nearest ten, i.e. 350, and then round to 100, i.e. 400. Pupils should be encouraged to read and round the whole number.

Practice activities

Use number cards (0 to 9). Take three cards to form a 3-digit number. Round the number made to the nearest ten and the nearest hundred. Repeat several times.

Use number cards (0 to 9). Take three cards to form a 3-digit number. Mark the number on a number line. Rearrange the digits to make another number that can be marked on the same number line.

Answers

1. 80   **2.** 300 and 400   **3.** 700   **4.** 30

6, **7**, **8**, **11** and **12** should be ticked

13. 109, 76 joined to 100   183, 245 joined to 200
254, 271, 349 joined to 300   350, 416, 432 joined to 400

Name _____

1. [ ]   **2.** [ ]   **3.** [ ]   **4.** [ ]

[ ]/4

Tick the numbers that have been rounded correctly
to the nearest 10.

5. 213 ⟶ 220   [ ]   **6.** 165 ⟶ 170   [ ]

7. 127 ⟶ 130   [ ]   **8.** 272 ⟶ 270   [ ]

9. 455 ⟶ 450   [ ]   **10.** 384 ⟶ 390   [ ]

11. 536 ⟶ 540   [ ]   **12.** 682 ⟶ 680   [ ]

[ ]/8

13. Join the numbers around the boxes to the nearest 100
(the 100 they should be rounded to).

271   416   109   245   350

| 100 | 200 | 300 | 400 |

183   76   349   432   254

[ ]/10

Score: [ ] /22   Total: [ ]

Addition and subtraction

Skills summary

- To add two 2- or 3-digit numbers using informal written methods
- To add two 2- or 3-digit numbers using standard written methods
- To subtract multiples of 10 from a 2- or 3-digit number

Diagnostic materials

Number Textbook 2, page 31, bottom section
- Check pupils can use knowledge of addition and place-value to find pairs of numbers with a total of 500.

Number Textbook, page 33
- Check pupils are able to subtract a 2-digit multiple of 10 from a 3-digit number.

Oral questions

1. Find the total of 124 and 36. (Write the numbers on the board.)

2. What is 35 more than 245? (Write the numbers on the board.)

3. I have £1·74 in my purse and I spend 80p. How much do I have left? (Write the numbers on the board.)

4. Subtract 60 from 326. (Write the numbers on the board.)

Common difficulties

Ensure that children understand the routine as well as learn it. It is important that they read the questions even when they are written in a vertical format and that they are encouraged to keep the place-value of the digits. Some children will benefit from using the expanded method first, e.g.

$$\begin{array}{r} 167 \\ + \ 244 \\ \hline 11 \\ 100 \\ 300 \\ \hline 411 \end{array}$$

It is useful when carrying out the calculation to read the value of the digits, i.e. *Seven and four is eleven, sixty and forty is one hundred, one hundred and two hundred is three hundred.*

Practice activities

1 Use number cards (0 to 9). Generate two 3-digit numbers by rolling dice or choosing number cards. Find the total of the two numbers by using either informal or standard written methods.

2 Use number cards (0 to 9 and 10, 20, ... 90). Generate a 3-digit number by rolling dice or choosing number cards. Take a number card with a multiple of 10 and subtract it from the 3-digit number. Write down the calculation and the answer.

Answers

1. 160	**2.** 280	**3.** 94p	**4.** 266
5. 386	**6.** 633	**7.** 534	**8.** 291
9. 437	**10.** 585	**11.** 762	**12.** 127
13. 50	**14.** 80	**15.** 184	**16.** 268
17. 425			

Name _____

1. [ ]   2. [ ]   3. [ ]   4. [ ]

4

Calculate the answer to these additions.
Show your calculation in the box.

5.	247 + 139
6.	362 + 271
7.	186 + 348

3

Complete these additions.

8.   164
     + 127
     _____

9.   285
     + 152
     _____

10.   238
      + 347
      _____

11.   373
      + 389
      _____

4

Fill in the missing numbers.

12. 157 − 30 = _____

13. 241 − _____ = 191

14. 263 − _____ = 183

15. _____ − 50 = 134

16. 358 − 90 = _____

17. _____ − 40 = 385

6

Score: [ ] /17   Total: [ ]

Subtraction

Skills summary

- To subtract a 2- or 3-digit number from a 3-digit number using informal methods
- To subtract a 2- or 3-digit number from a 3-digit number using a standard written method

Diagnostic materials

Number Textbook 2, page 36, questions 1 to 14

- Check pupils are able to calculate the answer to subtractions using complementary addition or other informal methods.

Number Textbook 2, page 41

- Check pupils can set out column subtractions accurately.

Oral questions

1. Subtract 67 from 80.

2. Find the difference between 86 and 103.

3. A carton of milk holds 500 ml. If 270 ml are used, how much milk is left?

4. (Write 596 – 109 on the board.) Look at the question. Write an approximate answer (i.e. to the nearest 100).

Common difficulties

Children who learn the routine without any understanding often forget stages in the process. It is important to provide apparatus to help them e.g. using a number line for informal written methods can help to develop a mental image. Using Base Ten material for subtraction to demonstrate the exchange from tens to units, or hundreds to tens can support the written method.

Pupils can be held back if they do not know their subtraction facts within 20. These need to be practised regularly so that the children do not return to counting on their fingers.

Practice activities

1 Use number cards (0 to 9). Take six cards to form two 3-digit numbers. Arrange the digits to try to find the largest difference between the two numbers. Write down the calculations and carry out the subtractions using formal or informal methods.

2 Roll a ten-sided dice three times to generate a 3-digit number. Write the number down. Repeat to generate another number. Subtract the smaller number from the larger one using informal or formal written methods.

Answers			
1. 13	**2.** 17	**3.** 230 ml	**4.** 500
5. 89	**6.** 158	**7.** 119	**8.** 117
10, 11 should be ticked		**9.** 126	**12.** 268

Name _____

1.   2.   3.   4.

$$\frac{\boxed{}}{4}$$

Calculate the difference between the numbers shown.
Show your calculation in the box.

5. 154 – 65

6. 237 – 79

7. 257 – 138

8. 316 – 199

$$\frac{\boxed{}}{4}$$

Tick the calculations that are correct.
Redo the calculations that are incorrect.

9.
```
  262
- 136
─────
  134   □
```

10.
```
  348
- 153
─────
  195   □
```

11.
```
  418
- 257
─────
  161   □
```

12.
```
  435
- 167
─────
  332   □
```

$$\frac{\boxed{}}{6}$$

Score: □ /14   Total: □

Odd and even numbers

Skills summary

- To recognise odd and even numbers to 1000
- To use knowledge of sums/differences of odd/even numbers
- To recognise and continue sequences of odd and even numbers

Diagnostic materials

Number Textbook 2, page 42, questions 15 to 27

- Check pupils are able to count up through even numbers and recognise even numbers as every other number.

Number Textbook 2, page 44, top section

- Check pupils can complete the subtraction table and recognise whether the answers to subtractions are odd or even.

Oral questions

1. Listen to these numbers: 127, 346, 245. Which one is even?

2. Add 26 and 43. Is the answer odd or even?

3. Subtract 17 from 45. Is the answer odd or even?

4. Will the total of 13, 15, 17 be odd or even?

Common difficulties

Some children are confused by a mixture of odd and even digits in a number. They need to recognise that the units digit is the most important when looking at odd and even numbers. Demonstrate that this is because all multiples of 10 and 100 are divisible by 2 therefore it is only really necessary to look at the units digit.

Give children opportunities to look at questions that have the wrong answer, e.g. they have an odd number answer when it should be even. Discuss whether they know if answers should be odd or even without calculating the answer but just by using their knowledge of odd and even numbers.

Practice activities

1 Use number cards (10 to 99). Choose two cards. Write down the numbers and decide whether the total will be odd or even. Repeat. Extend to decide whether the difference will be odd or even.

2 Roll a ten-sided dice twice. Write down the 2-digit number generated. If it is odd, write down the next two odd numbers. If it is even, write down the next two even numbers.

Answers

1. 346	**2.** odd	**3.** even	**4.** odd

5. 261, 483, 373, 117, 359, 825 should be circled

6. 114, 116, 118	**7.** 341, 339, 337		
8. 265, 263, 261	**9.** 498, 500, 502		

11, 12, 13 and **14** should be completed

11. 66	**12.** 70	**13.** 12	**14.** 8

Name _____

I. [ ]   **2.** [ ]   **3.** [ ]   **4.** [ ]

[ ] / 4

---

5. Circle the numbers that are odd.

352   261   483   560   373   734

117   359   825   378   604   778

[ ] / 6

Write 3 more numbers to continue each sequence.

6. 106, 108, 110, 112, _____, _____, _____

7. 349, 347, 345, 343, _____, _____, _____

8. 273, 271, 269, 267, _____, _____, _____

9. 490, 492, 494, 496, _____, _____, _____

[ ] / 12

Only complete calculations that give **even** number answers.

10. 27 + 34 = _____   **II.** 31 + 35 = _____

12. 44 + 26 = _____   **13.** 23 – 11 = _____

14. 36 – 28 = _____   **15.** 35 – 18 = _____

[ ] / 6

Score: [ ] /28   Total: [ ]

Negative numbers

Skills summary

- To recognise negative numbers in context
- To read and position negative numbers on a number line
- To count back including past zero
- To calculate a temperature rise or fall

Diagnostic materials

Number Textbook 2, page 45, questions 1 to 7
- Check pupils are able to read temperatures shown on a thermometer scale.

Number Textbook 2, page 46, number line
- Check pupils are able to use the number line to subtract a given number from each number shown including those with an answer below zero.

Oral questions

1. Write the number one less than -3.

2. (Draw a thermometer on the board with -5 marked.) What is the reading on the thermometer?

3. The temperature increases during the day from -7 °C to -4 °C. How many degrees has the temperature risen?

4. What is 5 more than -2?

Common difficulties

Give children lots of practice in counting forwards and backwards, including below zero, to ensure that they feel confident with negative numbers. Those who are less confident with negative numbers will often confuse positive and negative. Provide resources that will develop visual imagery, such as number lines that continue into negative numbers, and point to the negative numbers as they are said.

Practice activities

1 Draw a number line with -10 and 10 marked at the ends. Roll two ten-sided dice, a blue dice for negative numbers and a red dice for positive numbers. Roll each dice four times and mark the negative and positive numbers on the line.

2 Use number cards (0 to 9). Take two cards. Subtract the larger number from the smaller one, e.g. 4 – 7, and calculate the answer, i.e. -3, using a number line to help if necessary.

Answers			
1. -4	**2.** -5 °C	**3.** 3 °C	**4.** 3
5. 2 °C	**6.** -5 °C	**7.** -3 °C	**8.** 1 °C
5a. 0 °C	**6a.** -7 °C	**7a.** -5 °C	**8a.** -1 °C
9. <	**10.** >	**11.** >	**12.** <
13. 1, 0, -1	**14.** 1, 3, 5	**15.** 2, 0, -2	

Name _____

1.    2.   3.   4.

$\dfrac{\Box}{4}$

Write the temperature shown on each thermometer.

5. 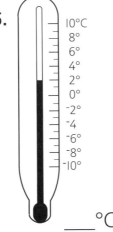   6. 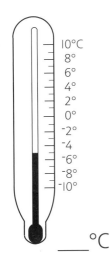   7. 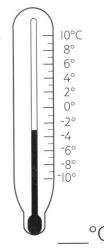   8.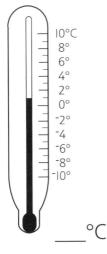

___°C   ___°C   ___°C   ___°C

The temperature falls by 2 °C in each case. Write the new temperature.

5a. ___°C   **6a.** ___°C   **7a.** ___°C   **8a.** ___°C

$\dfrac{\Box}{8}$

Put in the correct sign: < or >.

9. ⁻3 °C $\Box$ 5 °C   **10.** 3 °C $\Box$ ⁻2 °C

11. 2 °C $\Box$ ⁻6 °C   **12.** ⁻7 °C $\Box$ 4 °C

$\dfrac{\Box}{4}$

Fill in the missing numbers.

13. 6   5   4   3   2   ___   ___   ___

14. ⁻9   ⁻7   ⁻5   ⁻3   ⁻1   ___   ___   ___

15. 12   10   8   6   4   ___   ___   ___

$\dfrac{\Box}{9}$

Score: $\Box$ /25   Total: $\Box$

Multiplication

Skills summary
- To double multiples of 10 to 500
- To double multiples of 100 to 5000
- To derive quickly halves corresponding to doubles of multiples of 10 to 500 and of 100 to 5000
- To multiply a 2-digit by a 1-digit number using an expanded written method

Diagnostic materials
Number Textbook 2, page 50, top section
- Check pupils can use doubling and halving to solve simple problems.

Number Textbook 2, page 51, questions 1 to 10
- Check pupils can set out vertical 2-digit by 1-digit multiplications and can carry out the expanded written method.

Oral questions
1. Double 260.
2. I am thinking of a number. I double it. The answer I get is 640. What number am I thinking of?
3. Half of a number is 1800. What is the number?
4. What is 31 multiplied by 4?

Common difficulties
Children unsure of their knowledge of doubles up to 50 are likely to struggle when doubling multiples of 10 and 100. They need to practise doubling and halving and to partition the number into tens and units in order to make doubling easier. Once they are more confident with doubles to 50 they can then use their knowledge of 2-digit number doubles to double multiples of 10 to 500 and multiples of 100 to 5000. E.g. if you know that double 18 is 36, then double 180 is 360 and double 1800 is 3600.

In the same way, point out to children the connections between tables and the multiplication of multiples of 10, e.g. 4 x 6 = 24, 4 x 60 = 240.

Practice activities

1 Use number cards (10 to 50). Take a card. Write down the number, e.g. 38, and its double, i.e. 76. Then write the number and its double as a multiple of 10, i.e. 380 and 760, and then as a multiple of 100, i.e. 3800 and 7600.

2 Use number cards (10 to 99). Take a card and roll a ten-sided dice to generate a 2-digit by 1-digit multiplication. Write the vertical calculation and calculate the answer using the expanded written layout.

Answers
1. 520	**2.** 320	**3.** 3600	**4.** 124

5. reading from left to right 460, 740, 420, 270, 3200, 3900

6. 90	**7.** 160	**8.** 280	**9.** 700
10. 1700	**11.** 3500		

14, **15**, **16** and **17** should be ticked

Name _____

1.   **2.**   **3.** [ ] **4.** [ ]

[ ] / 4

5. The machine doubles the number put in.

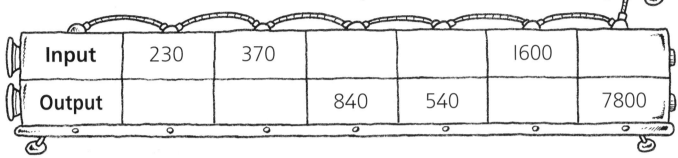

Input	230	370			1600	
Output			840	540		7800

[ ] / 6

Halve each of the numbers shown.

6. 180 _____   **7.** 320 _____   **8.** 560 _____

9. 1400 _____   **10.** 3400 _____   **11.** 7000 _____

[ ] / 6

Tick the calculations that are correct.

12.
```
    26
 x   3
    12
    60
    62
```
[ ]

13.
```
    31
 x   4
     4
    12
    16
```
[ ]

14.
```
    43
 x   3
     9
   120
   129
```
[ ]

15.
```
    48
 x   5
    40
   200
   240
```
[ ]

16.
```
    52
 x   4
     8
   200
   208
```
[ ]

17.
```
    67
 x   6
    42
   360
   402
```
[ ]

[ ] / 6

Score: [ ] / 22   Total: [ ]

Division

Skills summary

- To find remainders after division
- To decide whether to round up or down after division
- To use informal written methods for division
- To use standard written methods for division

Diagnostic materials

Number Textbook 2, page 55

- Check pupils are able to find remainders after division, 2-digit by 1-digit numbers, using multiplication lists or a tables square if necessary.

Number Textbook 2, page 58, questions 1 to 11

- Check pupils are able to set out and carry out a standard written method appropriately.

Oral questions

1. What remainder is left when 26 is divided by 4?

2. 5 friends share 17 sweets. If they all receive an equal amount, what is the highest number of sweets they can each have?

3. 4 cakes fit in a box. Gerry bakes 19 cakes. How many boxes will be needed to carry all the cakes?

4. How many 3s in 45? Jot down your working if you need to.

Common difficulties

Without a rapid recall of multiplication facts, each fact has to be worked out separately every time. Give those children without such a recall strategies to help them, such as counting in multiples of different sizes. Also encourage them to learn the facts by making the connections between them, e.g. the 4s are double the 2s, etc.

Children are easily confused about when to round up and when to round down. Work through the problems step by step; draw pictures or use the children to model the problems.

Practice activities

1 Use number cards (10 to 40). Take a card and roll a dice to generate the divisor (if 1 is rolled, roll again). Write down the division, e.g. 23 ÷ 3 =, and calculate the answer including the remainder.

2 Use number cards (50 to 99). Take a card and roll a dice to generate the divisor. Try and calculate the answer using informal methods; otherwise use a standard written method.

Answers

1. 2	**2.** 3	**3.** 5	**4.** 15

5. 13, 37 joined to 1,   26, 50 joined to 2,   45, 21 joined to 3,
16, 40 joined to 4,   41, 23 joined to 5   **6.** 24   **7.** 16

8. 14	**9.** 23	**10.** 7, should be ticked	**11.** 6

Name _____

I. [ ] **2.** [ ] **3.** [ ] **4.** [ ]

[ ] / 4

5. Join each number to its remainder after it has been divided by 6.

45   50

16   21   13

| 1 | | 2 | | 3 | | 4 | | 5 |

37   40   41

26   23

[ ] / 10

Calculate the answer to each division. Show your calculation in the box.

| **6.** 72 ÷ 3 | **7.** 64 ÷ 4 |
| **8.** 84 ÷ 6 | **q.** 92 ÷ 4 |

[ ] / 4

Work out the answers, then decide whether they need to be rounded **up** or **down**. Tick if the answer should be rounded **up**.

10. Children sit in groups of 4 at tables. There are 27 children. How many tables are needed? _____ [ ]

II. Simon wants to buy stickers with his pocket money. They cost 8p per packet. He has 50p. How many can he buy? _____ [ ]

[ ] / 4

Score: [ ] /22   Total: [ ]

Fractions and decimals

Skills summary

- To use decimal notation for tenths
- To recognise one-place decimal numbers on a number line
- To use decimal notation for hundredths
- To recognise equivalence between simple fractions and decimals

Diagnostic materials

Number Textbook 2, page 60, questions 1 to 10
- Check pupils can recognise what fraction of each shape is shaded and write the number of tenths as a decimal.

Number Textbook 2, page 63, questions 11 to 13
- Check pupils can recognise one-place decimal numbers on a number line.

Oral questions

1. Write four tenths as a decimal.
2. Listen to this sequence: 0·8, 0·9, 1, 1·1. Which number comes next?
3. Write as a decimal the number halfway between 1 and 2.
4. What is 25 hundredths as a decimal?

Common difficulties

Make the equivalence between fractions and decimals very clear to the children and also the value of the digits in the tenths column. Children who do not fully understand may write $\frac{3}{10}$ as 3·10.

When first introduced to two-place decimals children often find it very difficult to understand that a number with more digits may be worth less than a number with fewer digits e.g. 0·5 is worth more than 0·37. Use Base Ten material (100 block to represent a whole one, 10 rods to represent tenths, and unit cubes to represent hundredths) so that children can see that 5 tenths is bigger than 3 tenths and 7 hundredths. Coins, such as £1, 10p and 1p, can also provide a visual representation. Numbers can also be built up using decimal arrow cards to show that 1·45 is 1 and 0·4 and 0·05, etc.

Practice activities

1 Roll a six-sided dice twice. Use the numbers rolled to form a one-place decimal, e.g. 3·5, then write this as a whole number and a fraction, i.e. $3\frac{5}{10}$.

2 Use number cards (0 to 9). Take a card then two more to form a two-place decimal number. Write the number on a number line. Keep the same starting digit (the whole number) and take two more cards. Write the new two-place decimal number on the number line. Repeat several times.

Answers

1. 0·4	**2.** 1·2	**3.** 1·5	**4.** 0·25

5–8. check numbers are positioned correctly

9. 3 and 0·6	**10.** 0·9 and 0·02	**11.** 4 and 0·2	**12.** 2 and 0·06
13. 0·5	**14.** 0·3	**15.** 0·37	
16. $\frac{6}{10}$ or $\frac{3}{5}$	**17.** $1\frac{2}{10}$ or $1\frac{1}{5}$	**18.** $2\frac{3}{4}$ or $2\frac{75}{100}$	

Name _____

1. [ ] **2.** [ ] **3.** [ ] **4.** [ ]

☐/4

Mark these decimals on the number line below.

5. 1·3   **6.** 0·7   **7.** 1·5   **8.** 0·25

0 |ʟ_ı_ı_ı_ı_ı_ı_ı_ı_ı_ı_| 1 |_ı_ı_ı_ı_ı_ı_ı_ı_ı_ı_ı| 2

☐/4

Circle the arrow cards needed to make each number.

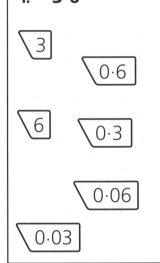 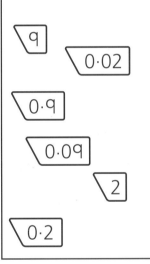 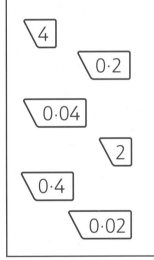

| 9. 3·6 | 10. 0·92 | 11. 4·2 | 12. 2·06 |

☐/4

Write the decimal equivalent of each of the numbers.

13. $\frac{1}{2}$ = _____   **14.** $\frac{3}{10}$ = _____   **15.** $\frac{37}{100}$ = _____

Write the fraction equivalent of each of the numbers.

16. 0·6 = _____   **17.** 1·2 = _____   **18.** 2·75 = _____

☐/6

Score: [ ]/18   Total: [ ]

Addition and subtraction

Skills summary

- To subtract a 3-digit number from a 3-digit number using a standard written method
- To add two-place decimals in the form of money
- To subtract two-place decimals in the form of money

Diagnostic materials

Number Textbook 2, page 67
- Check pupils can set out subtractions in a vertical layout putting the larger number above the smaller number and carry out a standard written procedure.

Number Textbook 2, page 69
- Check pupils can set out and follow written procedures to add or subtract amounts of money.

Oral questions

1. Approximate the answer to this subtraction to the nearest 100: 417 subtract 197.
2. What is the total of £2·50 and £1·75?
3. A book costs £4·75. How much change will there be from £10·00?
4. What must be added to £3·65 to make £5·00?

Common difficulties

Some pupils who do not understand the procedure will often forget or incorrectly order the steps when following a written method. Encourage pupils to estimate answers first so that they can recognise whether their answer is the correct size. Provide visual models to support the procedure, i.e. use Base Ten material to show the exchange from hundreds to tens or tens to units, or partition the numbers so that children can see what is happening to the numbers in decomposition, e.g.

$$
\begin{array}{ccc}
253 & \longrightarrow \quad 200 + 50 + 3 & \longrightarrow \quad 200 + 40 + 13 \\
137 & 100 + 30 + 7 & 100 + 30 + 7 \\
\hline
 & & 100 + 10 + 6 \\
\end{array}
$$

Practice activities

1 Take two items from a range priced between £1 and £2·50. Find the total of the items then calculate the change from £5·00.

2 Generate two 3-digit numbers by rolling a ten-sided dice. Subtract the smaller number from the larger one using a standard written method.

Answers

1. 200	**2.** £4·25	**3.** £5·25	**4.** £1·35
5. 214	**6.** 275	**7.** 155	**8.** 247

9. join a to i, b to h, c to j, d to f, e to g

10. £2·21	**11.** £1·46	**12.** £2·77

Name _____

1.   2.   3.   4.

4

Set out and complete the subtractions below.

5. 462 – 248 =   6. 528 – 253 =

7. 319 – 164 =   8. 624 – 377 =

4

9. Join amounts that total £5.

a £2·65   f £3·61

b £1·54   g £2·45

c £2·49   h £3·46

d £1·39   i £2·35

e £2·55   j £2·51

5

How much is left in each purse after spending £1·29?

10.    11.    12.

_____   _____   _____

3

Score: [   ] /16   Total: [   ]

Length

Skills summary

- To know and use the relationship between standard metric units of length – millimetres, centimetres, metres, kilometres
- To convert from one metric unit to another
- To recognise the mile as a unit of measure and its relationship with the kilometre

Diagnostic materials

Shape, Data and Measures Textbook, page 3
- Check pupils can estimate and measure using centimetres and millimetres.

Shape, Data and Measures Textbook, page 4
- Check pupils can convert measurements in metres or millimetres to centimetres.

Oral questions

1. How many centimetres are there in 2 m 50 cm?

2. Estimate the length of my thumb.

3. What unit of measurement would you use to measure the distance from this classroom to the hall?

4. Write 60 millimetres in centimetres.

Common difficulties

It is important that pupils have an understanding of the size of different units and their relationship to each other. They need to learn the key facts: 10 mm in 1 cm, 100 cm in 1 m, 1000 m in 1 km. When children work with other measures, e.g. grams and kilograms, point out the connections with units of length. Tell them that 'kilo' means 1000, so one kilometre = 1000 m, and one kilogram = 1000 g. They also need the opportunity to make estimates using benchmarks such as a metre stick or a ruler to compare with, and to decide on which unit or measure might be appropriate for a particular measurement.

Practice activities

1 Measure five items in the room in centimetres or millimetres. Then convert each of the lengths into metres and centimetres or centimetres and millimetres.

2 Use number cards (10, 15, 20, 25, ... 95). Take a card and write down the number as a number of kilometres. Convert it to a number of miles, e.g. 15 kms = 9 miles.

Answers

1. 250 cm   **2.** check the estimates are reasonable

3. check the unit of measurement is appropriate

4. 6 cm   **6, 7** and **9** should be ticked

5. 4·5 cm or $4\frac{1}{2}$ cm   **6.** 5·5 cm or $5\frac{1}{2}$ cm   **7.** 6 cm

8. 4 cm   **9.** 6·5 cm or $6\frac{1}{2}$ cm   **10.** 3·5 cm or $3\frac{1}{2}$ cm

11. 5 km, 3 miles   **12.** 10 000 m, 6 miles   **13.** 20 000 m, 12 miles

14. 15 000 m, 15 km

Name _____

1. [ ]   2. [ ]   3. [ ]   4. [ ]

$\frac{\quad}{4}$

Tick the lines that measure more than 50 mm.

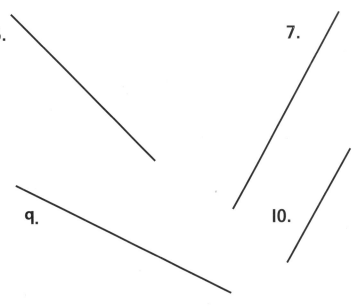

5.   6.   7.

8.   9.   10.

Write the length of each line (on the line) in centimetres.

$\frac{\quad}{12}$

Fill in the missing measurements below so that each is written in **metres**, **kilometres** and **miles**.

11. 5000 m ⟶ _____ km ⟶ _____ miles

12. _____ m ⟶ 10 km ⟶ _____ miles

13. _____ m ⟶ 20 km ⟶ _____ miles

14. _____ m ⟶ _____ km ⟶ 9 miles

$\frac{\quad}{8}$

Score: [ ] /24   Total: [ ]

Weight

Skills summary

- To recognise the relationship between familiar units of weight
- To convert weights in kilograms and grams to grams and vice versa
- To choose appropriate units of weight
- To estimate weight in grams and kilograms

Diagnostic materials

Shape, Data and Measures Textbook, page 7, questions 8 to 16
- Check pupils are able to use their knowledge of grams and kilograms to work out how many bags of each weight would weigh 2 kg.

Shape, Data and Measures Textbook, page 8, questions 1 to 8
- Check pupils can choose an appropriate unit of measurement for each object and make a reasonable estimate.

Oral questions

1. How many grams are there in one and a half kilograms?
2. Does a baby weigh about 400 g, 4 kg, or 40 kg?
3. Write two thousand five hundred grams in kilograms and grams.
4. From a 2 kg bag of flour, 250 g are used. How much flour is left in the bag?

Common difficulties

Pupils often find estimating weight difficult because, unlike length (and, to a certain extent, capacity) there is no visual benchmark with which to make comparisons, i.e. a larger object does not necessarily weigh more. Whenever the children's work involves estimation, ensure that they have a benchmark for comparisons, for example, a 1 kg weight or an object that weighs, a certain amount.

Practice activities

1 Choose five objects in the room that each weigh less than 1 kg. Estimate their weight using 250 g, 500 g and 1 kg weights, then check the actual weight of each object with a balance.

2 Use five or six supermarket items with the weights hidden. Order the items according to their weight, from lightest to heaviest. Check their actual weights using a balance.

Answers

1. 1500 g   **2.** 4 kg   **3.** 2 kg 500 g   **4.** 1750 g

5. 1300 g, 1 kg 300 g   **6.** 1750 g, 1 kg 750 g   **7.** 2600 g, 2 kg 600 g

8. 3150 g, 3 kg 150 g   **9.** 2750 g, 2 kg 750 g   **10.** 2350 g, 2 kg 350 g

11–14. check weights are marked accurately on each scale

Name _____

1.

2.

3.

4.

☐/4

Write the total weight for each question in g and in kg and g.

5.

____ g = __ kg ___ g

6.

____ g = __ kg ___ g

7.

____ g = __ kg ___ g

8.

____ g = __ kg ___ g

9.

____ g = __ kg ___ g

10.

____ g = __ kg ___ g

☐/12

Mark each of the amounts shown on the scale.

11. 1·5 kg

12. 1 kg 200 g

13. 2300 g

14. 2750 g

☐/4

Score: ☐ /20

Total: ☐

Capacity

Skills summary

- To recognise the relationship between familiar units of capacity
- To record readings from scales to a suitable degree of accuracy
- To convert litres and millilitres into millilitres and vice versa
- To recognise the approximate relationship between pints and litres

Diagnostic materials

Shape, Data and Measures Textbook, page 9, questions 1 to 9
- Check pupils are able to read the scale on each container and recognise that measuring jugs contain different amounts when full.

Shape, Data and Measures Textbook, page 11
- Check pupils are able to solve simple problems involving capacity.

Oral questions

1. How many litres are equal to two thousand millilitres?

2. Write three litres two hundred millilitres in millilitres.

3. A jug holds a litre of water. Three hundred millilitres of water are poured from the jug. How much water is left in the jug?

4. Approximately how many pints are there in five litres?

Common difficulties

As with any sort of measuring, children need to carry out a lot of practical work. Misconceptions, such as the taller the vessel the more it contains, must be confronted directly by using a wide variety of containers. When making estimates ensure that the children have a benchmark to make comparisons with, e.g. a litre container.

Some pupils find reading scales on measuring containers particularly difficult when the calibrations change, e.g. the scale has 50 ml divisions rather than 100 ml. Encourage pupils to talk about different divisions and how they should be read.

Practice activities

1 Using water, estimate and measure, using a litre jug, the capacity of six different containers. Record estimates and actual measures in a table.

2 Using water, measure the capacity of five small containers (each less than 200 ml). Calculate how many full containers would be needed to measure one litre of water. Check by filling a litre jug with water using each of the containers.

Answers

1. 2 l	**2.** 3200 ml	**3.** 700 ml	**4.** 10 pints

5–10. check capacities are marked correctly

11. 1000 ml	**12.** 8 pints	**13.** 5 pints	**14.** 2500 ml
15. 800 ml	**16.** $1\frac{1}{4}$ l or 1 l 250 ml or 1250 ml		**17.** 850 ml

Name _____

1.   2.   3.   4.

$\frac{\Box}{4}$

Mark the capacity shown on each measuring jug.

5. 250 ml   6. 800 ml    7. 1300 ml

8. 1500 ml    9. $1\frac{1}{4}$ l    10. $\frac{3}{4}$ l

$\frac{\Box}{6}$

Convert the capacities shown into an equivalent measure.

11.    12.    13.    14.

_____ ml   _____ pints   _____ pints   _____ ml

$\frac{\Box}{4}$

Write the amount left in each jug after the glass has been filled.

15.    16.    17.

_____   _____   _____

$\frac{\Box}{3}$

Score: $\boxed{}$ /17   Total: $\boxed{}$

Area and perimeter

Skills summary

- To understand area as 'covering' in two dimensions
- To measure area in square centimetres using counting methods
- To measure perimeter in centimetres
- To calculate perimeter in centimetres or metres

Diagnostic materials

Shape, Data and Measures Textbook, page 13
- Check pupils are able to find the approximate area of shapes that have some part squares.

Shape, Data and Measures Textbook, page 17, questions 1 to 6
- Check pupils are able to calculate the perimeter of rectangular plots from given dimensions.

Oral questions

1. Draw a square with an area of four square centimetres.
2. A rectangle is made up of four rows of five square centimetres. What is its area?
3. A square has sides six centimetres long. What is its perimeter?
4. A rectangle is seven centimetres long and two centimetres wide. Calculate the perimeter.

Common difficulties

As it is easy to lose count when counting shapes which cover parts of squares, encourage children to mark whole squares and count them first and then count the part squares.

When finding the perimeter of regular shapes encourage children to measure only some of the sides and to use these measurements to calculate. For example, to find the perimeter of a square measure one of the sides and multiply by 4. This can be extended for a rectangle by measuring one long and one short side, doubling each, then finding the total.

Practice activities

1 Draw shapes with an area of 12 cm² and calculate the perimeter. Find different lengths for the perimeter.

2 Draw shapes with a perimeter of 24 cm. Calculate the area of each. How many rectangles of different areas with sides of whole centimetre lengths have a perimeter of 24 cm?

Answers

1. check a 2 cm x 2 cm square has been drawn
2. 20 cm²   **3.** 24 cm   **4.** 18 cm
6 and **7** should be ticked
8. join a to h, b to i, c to l, d to k, e to g, f to j

Name _____

l. **2.**   **3.**   **4.**

$\frac{\boxed{}}{4}$

Tick the shapes which have an area of 12 cm².

5. 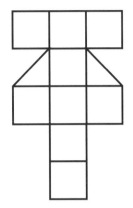 **6.** 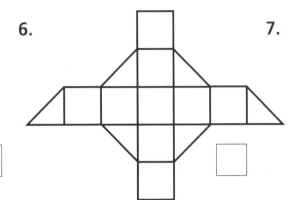 **7.**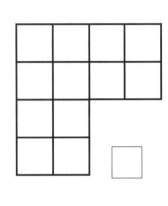

$\frac{\boxed{}}{3}$

8. Join each shape to its description. **g**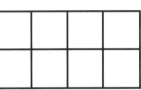

a area 6 cm², perimeter 10 cm

h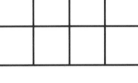

i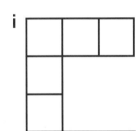

b area 8 cm², perimeter 18 cm

c area 9 cm², perimeter 20 cm

d area 9 cm², perimeter 12 cm

j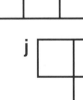

e area 8 cm², perimeter 12 cm

k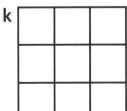

f area 6 cm², perimeter 12 cm

l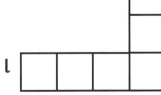

$\frac{\boxed{}}{6}$

Score: [   ] /13   Total: [   ]

Time

Skills summary

- To read the time from an analogue clock to the nearest minute
- To understand and use the notation 9:53
- To use a.m. and p.m. time
- To understand and read a timetable

Diagnostic materials

Shape, Data and Measures Textbook, page 19, questions 1 to 9
- Check pupils are able to read times to the nearest minute on analogue clocks.

Shape, Data and Measures Textbook, page 27
- Check pupils are able to extract information from a simple timetable and answer questions relating to it.

Oral questions

1. (Point to the classroom clock.) What time is it now?

2. I get up at 7 o'clock in the morning. Is that a.m. or p.m.?

3. A bus starts its journey at 9:20. The journey lasts 15 minutes. What time does it arrive at its destination?

4. A bus leaves one bus stop at 11:26. The next bus stop is 5 minutes away. What time does the bus arrive at the next stop?

Common difficulties

Children sometimes find it more difficult to read times before the hour than after the hour. They tend to be more used to reading digital displays that give times past the hour. Give children the opportunity to convert from one to the other, e.g. *9:45. How can we say that in a different way?* To do this, children need to feel confident with pairs of numbers that make 60.

When working with problems involving time, including reading a timetable, confusion often arises if times go over the hour, e.g. from 11:56 to 12:07. Remind children that there are 60 minutes in an hour and that they can then work out how many minutes to the hour and add on the number of minutes after the hour.

Practice activities

1 Use number cards (1 to 12, and 30 to 59). Take one card from each selection. The numbers create a time, e.g. 3:36. Write down the time and the equivalent time to the hour, i.e. 24 minutes to 4.

2 Use a bus timetable to calculate the journey time between stops. Use those journey times to work out another bus journey with a different starting time.

Answers

1. check pupils have written the correct time

2. a.m.   **3.** 9:35   **4.** 11:31

5–8. check hands are drawn on clock faces correctly

5. 8:25   **6.** 2:15   **7.** 4:40   **8.** 10:52

9. Post Office   **10.** Police Station   **11.** Town centre   **12.** Hospital

Name _____

1.   **2.**   **3.**   **4.**

$\dfrac{}{4}$

Write the time shown on each clock face.
Then write the time in digital form e.g. 7:35.

5. 25 past 8   [:]

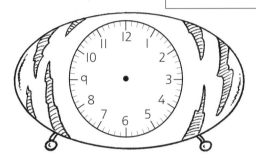

6. quarter past 2   [:]

7. 20 to 5   [:]

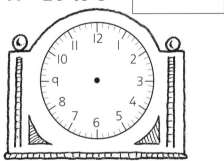

8. 8 minutes to 11   [:]

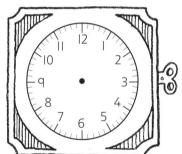

$\dfrac{}{8}$

Look at the bus timetable.
Where is the bus at the times shown?

9.

_____

10.

_____

11.

_____

12.

_____

Bus timetable	
Bus station	8:35
School	8:42
Hospital	8:50
Post Office	8:56
Leisure Centre	9:05
Police Station	9:10
Supermarket	9:18
Town centre	9:25

$\dfrac{}{4}$

Score: [   ] /16   Total: [   ]

M7 **M9** Time

Time

Skills summary

- To use and read a calendar
- To use and understand seconds as a unit of time
- To recognise that there are 60 seconds in 1 minute
- To estimate time in seconds

Diagnostic materials

Shape, Data and Measures Textbook, page 24
- Check pupils are able to order the months of the year and that they know how many days there are in each month.

Shape, Data and Measures Textbook, page 28
- Check pupils are able to interpret the number of seconds from an analogue stop watch.

Oral questions

1. Write down the name of the fifth month of the year.
2. The 1st of February is on a Monday. What day of the week is the 9th of February?
3. Which is longer: 100 seconds or one and a half minutes?
4. How many seconds are there in four minutes?

Common difficulties

Pupils need to know the order of the months and the number of days in each month. (Use the rhyme 'Thirty days hath September ...') To work out questions such as number 2 (above) the children also need to know how many days there are in the week and be comfortable with adding 7 to any number. Ask questions such as *Today is Monday the 7th. What will the date be next Monday?*

As with minutes and hours, to convert from seconds to minutes and vice versa pupils need to be confident with multiples of 60. Count in multiples of 6, then multiples of 60 so that pupils can make the connection.

Practice activities

1 Look at this year's calendar. Use it to find out what days of the week certain events fall on, e.g. your birthday, Christmas Day, New Year's Day, Bonfire Night.

2 Roll a ten-sided dice. If 1 is rolled convert 1 minute to seconds, if 2 is rolled convert 2 minutes into seconds, and so on. Write down the number of minutes and the equivalent number of seconds. How many conversions can be done in a minute?

Answers

1. May   **2.** Tuesday   **3.** 100 seconds   **4.** 240

5, 8, 9 and **10** should be ticked

11. 30 seconds   **12.** 35 seconds   **13.** 60 seconds   **14.** 85 seconds

Name _____

1. [   ]   2. [   ]   3. [   ]   4. [   ]

$\frac{\square}{4}$

Use the calendar to help decide
which statements are true.
Tick the statements that are true.

October

Sun	Mon	Tue	Wed	Thu	Fri	Sat
1	2	3	4	5	6	7
8	9	10	11	12	13	14
15	16	17	18	19	20	21
22	23	24	25	26	27	28
29	30	31				

5. October 11th is on a
   Wednesday. [   ]

6. There are 5 Wednesdays in the month of October. [   ]

7. In the same year 2nd November is on a Tuesday. [   ]

8. September 30th was on a Saturday. [   ]

9. November 5th falls on a Sunday. [   ]

10. 24th September was on a Sunday. [   ]

$\frac{\square}{6}$

Look at the stop watches. How many seconds are there between the
readings?

11.
mins secs		mins secs
00 : 15		00 : 45

12.
mins secs		mins secs
00 : 25		01 : 00

_____ seconds   _____ seconds

13.
mins secs		mins secs
01 : 45		02 : 45

14.
mins secs		mins secs
00 : 50		02 : 15

_____ seconds   _____ seconds

$\frac{\square}{4}$

Score: [   ] /14   Total: [   ]

Shape

Skills summary

- To recognise, name and construct 2-d shapes
- To recognise and use the term 'polygon'
- To classify regular and irregular polygons
- To recognise equilateral and isosceles triangles

Diagnostic materials

Shape, Data and Measures Textbook, page 33
- Check pupils are able to recognise and name polygons by using knowledge of the number of sides.

Shape, Data and Measures Textbook, page 35
- Check pupils are able to distinguish between regular and irregular polygons.

Oral questions

1. Circle, square, triangle – which of these shapes is not a polygon?
2. I am thinking of a shape. It is a polygon with five sides. Name the shape.
3. (Draw five shapes on the board, four regular, one irregular. Number them 1 to 5.) Which of these is an irregular shape?
4. What sort of triangle has three sides of equal length?

Common difficulties

Make it clear to children that hexagons, pentagons and so on are not necessarily regular. They will probably regard hexagons only as regular shapes rather than any six-sided shape. Give children opportunities to see both regular and irregular polygons and to discuss names and properties of the polygons. Similarly, when classifying triangles pupils need to see different isosceles triangles in a range of orientations.

Practice activities

1 Roll a six-sided dice. If a 3 or higher is rolled draw a polygon with that number of sides. Repeat several times ensuring that each polygon is different.

2 Use some geoboard paper. Within squares of 5 x 5 dots, draw isosceles triangles. How many different isosceles triangles can be drawn?

Answers

1. circle   **2.** pentagon
3. check the pupils have chosen the irregular shape   **4.** equilateral
5. a, c, d, e, f, h should be shaded
  a regular octagon   **c** regular pentagon   **d** irregular octagon
  e irregular hexagon   **f** regular hexagon   **h** irregular pentagon
6–9. check two sides have been added to the original side to form each triangle

---

Name _____

1.   **2.**   **3.**   **4.**

$\dfrac{}{4}$

5. Shade the shapes that are polygons.

a  b 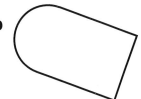 c  d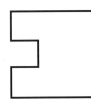

e   f 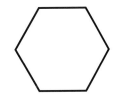 g 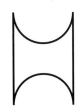 h

Below each polygon write its name and whether it is regular or irregular.
E.g. regular pentagon.

$\dfrac{}{14}$

Draw in the other two sides for each of the triangles below so that they
are isosceles or equilateral triangles.

6.

isosceles

7.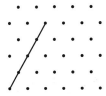

equilateral

8.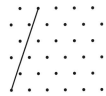

equilateral

q.

isosceles

$\dfrac{}{4}$

Score: _____ /22   Total: _____

Symmetry

Skills summary

- To understand the concept of line symmetry
- To recognise line symmetry in polygons
- To sketch the reflections of a simple shape in a mirror line

Diagnostic materials

Shape, Data and Measures Textbook, page 38
- Check pupils can recognise whether lines of symmetry are drawn correctly.

Shape, Data and Measures Textbook, page 40
- Check pupils are able to complete simple symmetrical patterns by reflection in the mirror line.

Oral questions

1. How many lines of symmetry are there in a rectangle?
2. (Draw an isosceles triangle on the board.) Copy the triangle and draw a line of symmetry on it.
3. Which has more lines of symmetry, a circle or a square?
4. (Draw a simple shape and a mirror line on the board.) Copy this shape and reflect it in the mirror line.

Common difficulties

Some children might not be able to recognise a line of symmetry or visualise how a shape might be reflected, e.g. they might think there is a line of symmetry along the diagonal of a rectangle. Encourage children to cut shapes out and fold them to check where the lines of symmetry are. They could also use a mirror to check accuracy.

When reflecting shapes children sometimes do not realise that the reflection should be the same distance away from the mirror line as the shape being reflected. This can be demonstrated with a mirror.

Practice activities

1 Draw around different templates of polygons and cut them out. Predict how many lines of symmetry each polygon has, then fold the shapes to check.

2 On a piece of squared paper, draw a mirror line. On one side of the mirror line draw a shape using five squares. Reflect the shape in the mirror line. Repeat several times.

Answers

1. 2   2. check the line of symmetry has been drawn correctly

3. circle   4. check the shape has been reflected correctly in the mirror line

5. 0 lines: a, e   1 line: b, f   2 lines: c, h   4 lines: d, g

6–8. check the lines of symmetry have been drawn correctly

6. 3 lines   7. 1 line   8. 2 lines

11 and 12 should be ticked

Name _____

1.    **2.**   **3.**   **4.**

☐/4

5. Join the shapes to the correct number of lines of symmetry.

 a      0 lines   **b**

c    1 line   **d**

e    2 lines   **f**

g   4 lines   **h**

☐/8

Draw lines of symmetry on these shapes.

6. 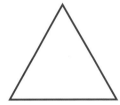   **7.** 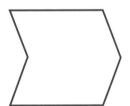   **8.**

☐/3

Tick the shapes that have been reflected correctly in the mirror line.

9. 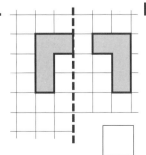   **10.** 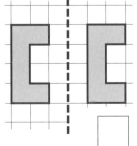   **11.** 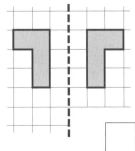   **12.**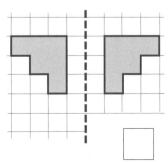

☐   ☐   ☐   ☐

☐/4

Score: ☐/19   Total: ☐

3-d Shape

Skills summary

- To recognise and use the names of common 3-d shapes
- To use the terms 'polyhedron' and 'tetrahedron'
- To understand the concept of a net and use it to construct common 3-d shapes

Diagnostic materials

Shape, Data and Measures Textbook, page 41
- Check pupils are able to recognise which nets will make a cube by using 3-d construction apparatus if necessary.

Shape, Data and Measures Textbook, page 43
- Check pupils are able to distinguish between pyramids and prisms.

Oral questions

1. How many faces are there on a cube?
2. I am thinking of a 3-d shape. It has four triangular faces and one square face. It also has five vertices and eight edges. Name the shape.
3. (Hold up a triangular prism.) What is this shape called?
4. If I put two cubes together, so that one face connects to another face, what new 3-d shape do they make?

Common difficulties

Some children have difficulty visualising what a net will look like when it is put together and also thinking about what the net of a 3-d shape might look like. They need to have plenty of practical experience using construction equipment such as Clixi or Polydron. They should be encouraged to talk about why a net may or may not work. Use a net and fold it partially and discuss where the other faces will be when the shape is fully constructed.

Practice activities

1. Investigate different prisms or pyramids. Make a table of their properties, e.g. the number of faces, edges, vertices, etc. Is there a relationship between the number of faces, vertices and edges?

2. Choose a 3-d shape. Make a net for it using Clixi or Polydron and then make a copy of the net using card.

Answers

1. 6   2. square-based pyramid   3. triangular prism
4. cuboid
5. a to i, b to h, c to f, d to g, e to j
7, 9 and 10 should be ticked
6. hexagonal prism   7. square-based pyramid   8. cube
9. triangular-based pyramid   10. hexagonal-based pyramid
11. triangular prism

Name _____

I.    **2.**   **3.**   **4.**

$\dfrac{\square}{4}$

5. Join each shape to its net.

a   **b**    **c**   **d**   **e**

f 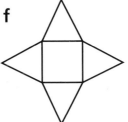   **g** 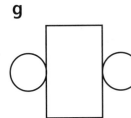   **h** 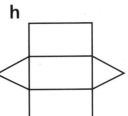   **i** 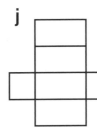   **j**

$\dfrac{\square}{5}$

Name each of the shapes below.
Tick the shapes that are pyramids.

6. ☐   **7.** ☐   **8.** ☐

_____ _____ _____

q. ☐   **10.** ☐   **II.** ☐

_____ _____ _____

$\dfrac{\square}{12}$

Score: ☐ /2I   Total: ☐

Direction and angle

Skills summary

- To recognise and measure right angle turns
- To recognise and use eight-point compass directions
- To measure angles using eight-point compass directions
- To use the degree as a unit of measure
- To understand and use the relationship between degrees and right angles

Diagnostic materials

Shape, Data and Measures Textbook, page 45

- Check pupils are able to work out the direction needed to get from one point to another.

Shape, Data and Measures Textbook, page 48

- Check pupils are able to recognise the direction an object will be facing after turns of a given number of right angles.

Oral questions

1. I am facing north. I turn two right angles clockwise. Which direction am I facing now?

2. To turn from facing west to facing south, how many right angles would I have to turn in a clockwise direction?

3. An hour hand is pointing to 2 o'clock. If it turns one right angle clockwise which hour will it point to?

4. I turn 270°. How many right angles is that?

Common difficulties

Children often struggle to remember directions and their relationship to one another. It is useful to use mnemonics such as *Never Eat Slimy Worms*. Play games in P.E. which require pupils to run to north, south, east or west.

Children need to be clear that an angle is a measurement of turn. Activities where they have to turn themselves or turn something else, such as directing one another around the classroom, help them to understand the concept.

Practice activities

1 Use direction cards (N, NE, E, SE, S, SW, W, NW). Take two cards and write down the directions chosen (e.g. S, NW). Write down the number of right angles needed to turn clockwise from facing one direction to the other (i.e. $1\frac{1}{2}$ right angles).

2 On an 8 x 8 grid mark eight arrows, placing each one in a different square, and facing different directions. Label the arrows 1 to 8. Describe how each arrow would have to move to get to the position of its nearest neighbour.

Answers					
1. south	**2.** 3		**3.** 5 o'clock	**4.** 3	
5. S	**6.** NE	**7.** W	**8.** SW	**9.** NW	**10.** E
11. a	**12.** c		**13.** b	**14.** a	

Name _____

1.   2.   3.   4.

$\frac{}{4}$

Write the direction from one town to another.

5. Blackpool to Liverpool _____

6. Liverpool to Bradford _____

7. Leeds to Blackpool _____

8. Leeds to Manchester _____

9. Manchester to Blackpool _____

10. Blackpool to Leeds _____

$\frac{}{6}$

Circle the arrow that is pointing in the correct direction after turning.

11. turn 2 right angles clockwise   a ⇦   b ⇧   c ⇩

12. ⇧ turn 3 right angles clockwise   a ⇨   b ⇩   c ⇦

13. ⇩ turn 3 right angles anticlockwise   a ⇧   b ⇦   c ⇨

14. ⇦ turn 1 right angle anticlockwise   a ⇩   b ⇧   c ⇨

$\frac{}{4}$

Score: _____ /14   Total: _____

Position

Skills summary

- To describe the position of a point on a grid where the horizontal and vertical lines are numbered
- To find the position of a point on a grid where the horizontal and vertical lines are numbered
- To recognise simple horizontal and vertical lines
- To understand and use the term 'coordinate'

Diagnostic materials

Shape, Data and Measures Textbook, page 50
- Check pupils are able to read the horizontal point marked by each ball and the vertical point marked by each ball.

Shape, Data and Measures Textbook, page 51
- Check pupils are able to read coordinates and use the correct notation to record their reading.

Oral questions

1. (Draw vertical and horizontal axes on the board. Mark the point (3,1) and point to it.) Write down the coordinates for this point.
2. Imagine the point (1,1). What are the coordinates of the point above it?
3. (Draw vertical and horizontal axes on the board without any labels. Draw a line parallel to the horizontal axis and mark the point (4,1) on the line.) This is the point (4,1). Write down another coordinate that would come on this line.
4. The points (1,1) (1,2) (1,3) (1,4) form a line. Is it a vertical or horizontal line?

Common difficulties

Children who are unclear about which coordinate to plot or read first will struggle with work on coordinates. They need to be reminded that they go across first. Mnemonics are useful: *Along the corridor and up the stairs, Crawl before you climb.*

Sometimes children can be confused as to whether it is the spaces or the lines that are labelled, particularly if they have done some grid reference work in geography. Remind them that they are labelling the lines.

Practice activities

1. Roll a ten-sided dice twice. Write down the coordinates, then plot the point. Repeat several times. Can the points be joined to form a picture?

2. Mark the points on a pair of (0–6) axes. Roll two six-sided dice to create coordinates. How many of the coordinates created are marked on the axes?

Answers

1. (3,1) 2. (1,2) 3. (__,1) 4. vertical
5. WHICH MONTH IS IT?
6. check coordinates for each letter have been read correctly
7. check points have been plotted correctly 8. (6,2) (4,0)

Name _____

1. [ ]   2. [ ]   3. [ ]   4. [ ]

☐
—
4

5. Crack the code using the letters on the grid.

(5,3) (2,1) (3,1) (3,0) (2,1)

___ ___ ___ ___ ___

(1,2) (3,2) (2,2) (2,3) (2,1)

___ ___ ___ ___ ___

(3,1) (1,3)   (3,1) (2,3)?

___ ___   ___ ___?

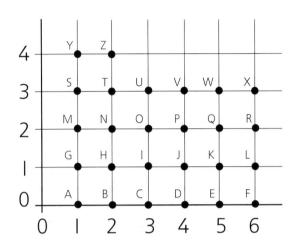

6. Spell out the answer to the coded question using coordinates.

_____

☐
—
15

7. Plot the points below on the grid.
(2,0) (0,2) (0,4) (2,6) (4,6) (6,4)

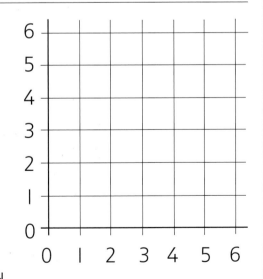

8. When joined in the order they are plotted
the points begin to form an octagon.
Write down the coordinates of the other
points needed to complete the shape.   (___ , ___) (___ , ___)

☐
—
8

Score: [ ] /27   Total: [ ]

Data

Skills summary

- To use tally charts to record data
- To represent data in a frequency table
- To interpret tally charts and frequency tables
- To construct and interpret a bar graph

Diagnostic materials

Shape, Data and Measures Textbook, page 54
- Check pupils are able to extract information from frequency tables and understand the vocabulary of comparison – most, fewest, etc.

Shape, Data and Measures Textbook, page 60
- Check pupils are able to construct bar graphs, including accurately drawing bars that fall between intervals.

Oral questions

1. Look at the bar graph. How many more people attended football club than chess club?

2. How many people altogether attended drama or table tennis?

3. Which club did the fewest people attend?

4. How many people attended the two most popular clubs?

Common difficulties

Children may not be clear about the vocabulary of comparison, e.g. how many more is ...? They often interpret 'more' as an indicator to add. Encourage them to make comparisons in a range of settings, to compare bars (in graphs), amounts of money, towers of cubes, etc.

Some children may find it hard to interpret and draw bars which come between intervals e.g. reading odd numbers where intervals are marked in 2s. Confront the problem directly: *We haven't got a 9 on the scale so where would we put the bar? Why?*

Give children some experience of bar graphs with horizontal bars.

Practice activities

1 Collect data (a possible homework activity) about favourite TV programmes, football teams, pop groups or hobbies etc. Write the frequency table and draw the bar chart with intervals labelled in 2s.

2 Take a bar chart or frequency table. Write six questions that can be answered using the information.

Answers

1. 3   **2.** 10   **3.** table tennis   **4.** 21

5. reading down the column: 11,   7,   10,   6,   9

pear, orange, banana bars should be ticked

6. reading down the column: 8,   5,   7,   10,   3

Name _____

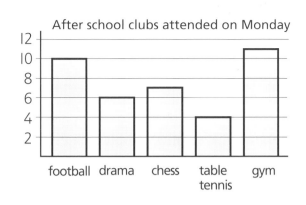

1. [ ]

2. [ ]

3. [ ]

4. [ ]

4

---

5. Use the tally chart to complete the frequency table to show people's favourite fruit.

Fruit	Tally	Total
apple	ⅢⅢ ⅢⅢ Ɩ	
pear	ⅢⅢ ǁ	
orange	ⅢⅢ ⅢⅢ	
banana	ⅢⅢ Ɩ	
peach	ⅢⅢ ǁǁǁ	

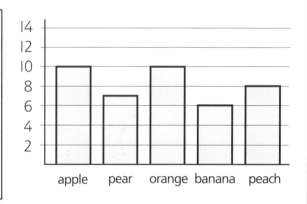

Tick the bars that are drawn correctly on the bar graph.

10

---

6. Use the bar chart to complete the frequency table of least favourite foods.

Food	Total
broccoli	
cheese	
sultanas	
mushrooms	
corned beef	

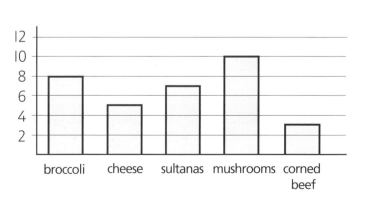

5

Score: [   ] /19   Total: [   ]

Data

Skills summary

- To construct and interpret a pictograph to represent data
- To construct and interpret Venn diagrams based on two intersecting sets of observations
- To construct and interpret Carroll diagrams

Diagnostic materials

Shape, Data and Measures Textbook, page 58
- Check pupils are able to construct a pictograph from given information where a symbol represents 3.

Shape, Data and Measures Textbook, page 64
- Check pupils are able to classify information using a Carroll diagram or a Venn diagram.

Oral questions

1. In a pictograph one complete symbol shows that 4 people chose a book. How many complete symbols would show that 12 people chose a book?
2. In the same pictograph there are $4\frac{1}{2}$ symbols in one column. How many people does this represent?
3. Look at the Carroll diagram. What do we know about Jack?
4. Sally has green eyes and brown hair. Which section would she go in? (Point to the sections.) Top left, top right, bottom left or bottom right?

Common difficulties

When drawing pictographs it is important to use a symbol that can be divided easily into equal parts. Pupils need to be confident with the multiples of the number the symbol represents, e.g. if each symbol represents 3 they need to know how many four symbols would make.

Confusion can arise with Carroll diagrams if children are not clear that the headings must be 'something' and 'not something' so that all possibilities are covered. If they use headings such as 'brown eyes' and 'blue eyes' there is nowhere to put green eyes.

Practice activities

1 Use data already collected for a survey e.g. favourite football teams, hobbies, etc. Draw a pictogram using a symbol to represent 3 or 4 people asked.

2 Make a Carroll diagram to classify 2-digit numbers. Pupils decide on criteria, e.g. multiple of 4, not multiple of 4, more than 50, not more than 50.

Answers

1. 3   2. 18   3. he has brown eyes but doesn't have brown hair
4. bottom left   5. 5   6. 10
7. 1   8. 4   9. check symbols are drawn accurately ($2\frac{1}{3}$ cones)
10. straight sides, curved sides

	brown hair	not brown hair
brown eyes	Sarah Patrick	Jack Sanjay Junko
not brown eyes	Bethan Joseph	Declan Michael

1. [ ]

2. [ ]

3. _____

_____

4. _____

4

The pictograph shows favourite ice-cream flavours.

represents 3 people.

How many people chose:

5. vanilla? _____

6. chocolate? _____

How many more chose:

7. chocolate than strawberry? _____

8. strawberry than vanilla? _____

9. 7 people chose raspberry ripple. Complete the
    pictograph to show this.

raspberry ripple

chocolate

flavour

strawberry

vanilla

number of people

5

10. Put headings on the diagram so that it makes sense.

_____   _____

2

Score: [ ] / 11   Total: [ ]

Record keeping

The record keeping grid list the units (or groups of units) assessed in this book. Across the top is room for up to fifteen names. Within each box on the grid is space to record the score each pupil achieved, so that over the course of the year you can easily track progress.

Names															
N1															
N2, N4															
N3, N5															
N6															
N7, N8															
N9, N10, N11															
N12, N13															
N14, N15															
N16															
N17, N18															
N19, N20															
N21															
N22, N23, N24															
N25, N26															
N27, N28															
N29															
N30, N31															
N32, N33															
N34															
N35															
N36, N37															
N38, N39															
N40, N41															
N42, N43															
M1															
M2															
M3															
M4, M5															
M6, M8															
M7, M9															
S1, S2															
S3															
S4															
S5, S6															
S7															
D1, D3															
D2, D4															